A SYMPOSIUM ON
pH AND BLOOD GAS
MEASUREMENT

Methods and Interpretation

A SYMPOSIUM ON
pH and Blood Gas Measurement

METHODS AND INTERPRETATION

Edited by

RONALD F. WOOLMER
V.R.D., B.A., B.M., F.F.A.R.C.S.

Professor of Anæsthetics in the
Royal College of Surgeons of England

Assisted by

JOY PARKINSON, B.A.

With 48 Illustrations

LONDON
J. & A. Churchill Ltd.
104 GLOUCESTER PLACE, W.1
1959

Printed in Great Britain

FOREWORD

THE hydrogen ion concentration of the blood is such a closely guarded aspect of the *milieu interne* that deviations of the order of a few hundredths of a pH unit are significant, and these are capable of detection with modern instruments.

The interaction between the lungs and the kidneys in the regulation of pH—working sometimes in harmony and sometimes in opposition—leads to complex situations whose understanding demands clarity of thought and whose explanation calls for an unambiguous notation.

The range of people concerned with hydrogen ion regulation is wide. It includes physicians, surgeons, anæsthetists, urologists, pædiatricians, clinical pathologists, biochemists and physicists; and it is because of this diversity that many people have been feeling the need for a common meeting ground.

To meet this need a group of people came together—experts from many different fields—to exchange ideas on means of measurement, to discuss their clinical significance and to consider how the abnormalities detected could be expressed most clearly to the clinician.

This volume contains the Report of that meeting. It brings together a wealth of information about a subject so diffuse that no textbook deals with it as an entity; and though it does not set out to cover every aspect fully, there are not many which escape mention in the discussion or in the references, even if they are not dealt with in one of the ten papers.

It is unfortunate that a printers' strike has delayed the appearance of this Report by a month or two. Messrs. J. & A. Churchill Ltd. are to be congratulated on the way in which they have dealt with all the difficulties.

R. F. W.

CONTENTS

PARTICIPANTS AT THE SYMPOSIUM ON pH
AND BLOOD GAS MEASUREMENT
2nd AND 3rd DECEMBER 1958

Dr. P. Astrup. Rigshospitalet, Copenhagen, Denmark.

Dr. J. Bishop. Department of Medicine, Queen Elizabeth Hospital, Edgbaston, Birmingham.

Mr. D. Brooks. Surgical Unit, St. Mary's Hospital, London.

Dr. E. J. M. Campbell. Department of Medicine, The Middlesex Hospital, London.

Dr. P. Cliffe. Department of Anæsthesia, Westminster Hospital, London.

Dr. I. C. Geddes. Department of Anæsthesia, University of Liverpool.

Dr. R. P. Harbord. 24 Hyde Terrace, Leeds, 2.

Mr. D. W. Hill. Department of Anæsthetics, Royal College of Surgeons of England.

Mr. M. Hobsley. Department of Surgical Studies, The Middlesex Hospital, London.

Mr. G. P. King. Chemical Applications Dept., W. G. Pye & Co. Ltd., Cambridge.

Dr. Lauchlan. Cambridge Instrument Co. Ltd., London.

Dr. B. G. B. Lucas. Surgical Unit, University College Hospital Medical School, London.

Dr. J. Macrae. Ham Green Hospital, Bristol.

Dr. G. Mattock. Electronic Instruments Ltd., Richmond, Surrey.

Professor E. Neil. Department of Physiology, Middlesex Hospital Medical School, London.

Dr. J. F. Nunn. Department of Anæsthetics, Royal College of Surgeons of England.

Professor E. A. Pask. Department of Anæsthetics, Royal Victoria Infirmary, Newcastle-on-Tyne.

Dr. J. P. Payne. Department of Anæsthetics, Postgraduate Medical School, London.

Dr. P. W. Ramwell. Bradford College of Technology, Bradford, Yorks.

Dr. C. F. Scurr. Department of Anæsthetics, Westminster Hospital, London.

Dr. J. W. Severinghaus. Cardiovascular Research Institute, University of California Medical Center, San Francisco.

Dr. M. K. Sykes. Department of Anæsthetics, Postgraduate Medical School, London.

Professor R. F. Woolmer. Department of Anæsthetics, Royal College of Surgeons of England.

Dr. M. Wright. Department of Clinical Biochemistry, Radcliffe Infirmary, Oxford.

Dr. V. Wynn. St. Mary's Hospital, London.

First Session

I. CHAIRMAN'S OPENING ADDRESS

As Chairman of this meeting I would like to express to the Ciba Foundation, here represented by Dr. Genese, our warm appreciation of their action in making this gathering possible. The quiet efficiency of their arrangements and the elegance of the surroundings combine to make it a real pleasure for us to attend this meeting here. A discussion group such as this owes a great deal of its success to the fact that it is small. This, of course, means that people who might properly have come to it have not been able to be invited. The selection has had to be entirely arbitrary. No two of us, I imagine, if asked to draw up a list, would make the same list, or even lists that were very similar. For sins of commission and omission in this respect I must take the blame, but I comfort myself with the thought on looking around me that we have not got such a bad group together.

II. PROBLEMS OF THE ANÆSTHETIST IN RELATION TO DISTURBANCES IN ACID-BASE EQUILIBRIUM

Ronald Woolmer

Professor of Anæsthesia, Royal College of Surgeons of England

As an anæsthetist my interest in acid base balance is mainly on the respiratory side. Modern techniques of anæsthesia and of surgery increasingly impair the ability of the respiratory system to maintain carbon dioxide homeostasis, so that this duty is falling more and more upon the anæsthetist. Many anæsthetists are ill-equipped both mentally and technically for this task. Few of them have much idea whether they are pushing their patients into respiratory acidosis or into respiratory alkalosis. It is extremely likely that they are pushing them into one or other of these two states because the chance of any anæsthetist with only his unaided senses to guide him setting the ventilation at just the right value for any patient must be pretty small. How often the effects of this carbon dioxide imbalance are disastrous is difficult to say. Probably not very often because the human body can put up with an astonishing amount of punishment. We must not forget, however, that many of the surgical patients with whom we have to deal are unable to produce a proper metabolic compensation for the respiratory imbalance we impose on them, because of kidney disease, or anæmia, or dehydration, or electrolyte imbalance. We have been interested, therefore, in the means of recognizing and of preventing carbon dioxide imbalance during anæsthesia. The anæsthetist's ideal for this, I suppose, would be a continuous indication of the arterial carbon dioxide tension. This, however, in the operating room is not generally feasible just yet and so we have to get at it indirectly by taking samples of respiratory gases, though this approximation is not nearly as satisfactory as we would like it to be. The other approach is perhaps a good deal easier. For this we do not measure the arterial P_{CO_2}, or even estimate it indirectly; but we measure the ventilation. It should be possible from our knowledge of the state of the patient to predict what ventilation would be required to keep him in carbon dioxide homeostasis. If we could make this prediction with confidence we should be able to steer our patient along a trouble-free course because then all we would need would be a means of estimating and of controlling the minute volume of ventilation, and this in fact is not too difficult. When we looked into the reliability of such a prediction, however, we were disappointed to find that the correlation between the actual P_{CO_2} in a patient for different rates of ventilation with the predicted values for those rates was not nearly as high as we would have liked, and some figures that have been collected in my Department, largely by Dr. Nunn and Mr. Hill, show that there is a fairly wide divergence between the P_{CO_2} actually obtained with a given ventilation and the P_{CO_2} which we would predict. In spite of this, however, I think the correspondence between prediction and fact is generally good enough to enable us to keep our patient out of trouble in the great majority of cases, so that it may be that it is better to stick to this measurement which is comparatively easy than to try to do better and go after more or less direct estimates of P_{CO_2} which carry with them their own difficulties. It not infrequently happens that surgical patients who have been operated on with anæsthesia involving positive pressure artificial ventilation remain comatose and flaccid for quite long periods, and it is then necessary to work out their acid base balance and to try and decide in which direction it is disturbed. In this connection, of course, we have to bear in mind that the departure from homeostasis may be imposed on them not only by respiratory imbalance but by metabolic imbalance as well. So we have to ask ourselves: What information do we require in order to elucidate the acid base state of this patient, what resources are needed to produce this information and how should the figures that we get be expressed in order to convey the greatest possible amount of information? Should we use the concept of buffer base or standard bicarbonate or carbon dioxide combining power, and so on? Should we use a pH/P_{CO_2} diagram or a pH/bicarbonate diagram or how are we going to express these figures? This is what we want to know and this is the sort of information which I hope will arise out of this meeting. We hope we may get some measure of agreement on this and we know that there will be an exchange of ideas between us on methods of measurement. Each of us here has a direct interest in acid base balance, but from a different point of view, and we hope that these different points of view will be put forward.

III. pH MEASUREMENTS WITH THE GLASS ELECTRODE

M. P. Wright, B.M., M.A.

Research Assistant to the Accident Service

From the Department of Clinical Biochemistry, Radcliffe Infirmary, Oxford

THE standard methods of measuring pH with the glass electrode have been quoted to an accuracy of $\pm$ 0·02 units for the last twenty-five years.   Recently, two new pH meters have appeared, each capable of a discrimination ten times better than this. Their appearance laid down a challenge: can an electrode system be made stable and reproducible enough to take full advantage of this improvement?   A number of people have taken up the challenge, and I am among them.

The electrode systems commonly used all share an identical basic pattern.   The glass membrane has on one side N/10 HCl, and on the other the test solution.   A reference electrode makes contact with the HCl, and a second reference electrode, in a constant reference solution, makes contact with the test solution through a liquid junction.   The potential between the two reference electrodes is measured by the pH meter.   Each of these links in the chain is a source of error, and each source of error can be whittled away.   My best results so far were repeatable to $\pm$ 50 microvolts, and there seemed to be no absolute limitation at this level.

To consider each link in turn:

(1) The pH Meter

The obvious limitations to a meter's performance are its zero stability, sensitivity and the accuracy of its dial calibration. But there are three other sources of error which are not so obvious.   The effect of the temperature control is to alter the constant of proportionality of voltage input to dial reading in pH units, while the asymmetry control alters the zero of the pH scale.   Thus it is vital that the fineness and accuracy of calibration of these controls should match or exceed that of the main dial. There are very few meters in which this is achieved. May I also put in a plea for the calibration of the temperature control directly in potential/pH ratio, instead of in °C.? It has lately become clear that in systems with a liquid junction, even when using a very good glass electrode, the observed potential/pH ratio is always greater than the theoretical value. With home-made capillary electrodes it may be much greater, due to imperfect insulation. Thus, if accuracy is to be maintained, this ratio must be set up directly and not allowed for approximately as a temperature. The alternative is to abandon these two controls and measure directly in millivolts.

Finally, the input impedance should be at least a thousand times that of the highest resistance electrode to be used. If it is not, then two effects are produced. Firstly, the input impedance acts as a shunt across the electrodes and the voltage measured is a fixed proportion of the true electrode potential. This is an important cause of deviation from the theoretical potential/pH ratio. Insulation leakages act in the same way, except that their resistance is not constant.

Secondly, lowering the input impedance, or allowing leakage pathways, increases the real current which flows through the electrode during measurement. This is almost certainly the reason why the potential of high resistance electrodes floats slowly and exponentially to approach, but never reach, a final value.

The two pH meters referred to earlier are the Vibron unit, made by Electronic Instruments, and the Doran precision meter.

The Vibron unit is mains-operated, direct-reading, and very convenient to use. For pH measurements, range switching, asymmetry and temperature controls are provided by a separate box. It is unfortunate that the temperature control acts stepwise, by a switch, so that it cannot be used to allow for deviations from the theoretical potential/pH ratio. Its input impedance and zero stability are high. Its absolute accuracy is limited by two factors. First, the inherent noise level produces a needle flicker of about 50–100 microvolts. Secondly, the linearity of any direct-reading meter is seldom better than 1 per cent of full-scale deflection. The quoted limits are $\pm 0\cdot1$ millivolts, or $0\cdot002$ pH units.

The Doran meter is a battery-operated electrometer valve

voltmeter, based on the Morton circuit. It is capable of greater accuracy than the Vibron unit, but readings take longer, since it is a nullreading instrument, and has to be standardized between readings. The smallest scale divisions on its potentiometer are 0·1 millivolts and a further place can be interpolated. The direct calibration is accurate to $\pm$ 50 microvolts and corrections can be applied from the calibration chart supplied.

The absolute limit to its accuracy is set by the stability of its valve current, whose drift sometimes amounts to 20 microvolts in the course of one reading. But a good deal of modification is required before this accuracy can be realized; all the ancillary controls have to be redesigned to increase their fineness of adjustment.

As the set was delivered, the standard deviation of successive readings of the E.M.F. of a Weston cell was 0·9 millivolts. After modification this figure was improved to 23 microvolts. The firm is incorporating a number of these improvements in later models. All my measurements have been made with this meter.

(2) Reference Electrodes

There are two theoretical points which indicate possible causes of instability in reference electrodes as they are commonly used:

First, if the electrode potential is controlled by the structure of the electrode surface, then electrodes, to be stable, should have uniform, stable, and reproducible surfaces. Following from this, also, the surface should always be completely immersed in the electrolyte. Secondly, if measurements are to be made to 0·001 units, then temperature stability must be better than $\pm$ 0·05 °C.

There are only two types of electrode commonly used; the calomel electrode, and the silver chloride electrode.

The ordinary commercial calomel electrode has a completely indeterminate electrode surface. They are stable enough for measurements to $\pm$ 1 millivolt, especially when kept at room temperature. But they may take weeks to come to equilibrium when put in a waterbath, and many show persistent drifts of six or seven millivolts a day, with superimposed random fluctuations of $\pm$ 0·2 millivolts. Dr. Mattock tells me, however, that E.I.L.'s calomel electrodes are stable to $\pm$ 0·1 millivolts.

Hills and Ives designed their special form of calomel electrode to overcome these difficulties. When carefully made, it is extremely stable; but it only works really well in hydrochloric acid, and it is rather too much trouble for routine use.

I have found silver chloride electrodes more satisfactory than either of these, and always use them instead of calomel electrodes. Their disadvantage is that they will not work in saturated KCl, because silver chloride is appreciably soluble in it. They are most stable in HCl, but they will remain stable for a week or two in N/10 NaCl or KCl. They are stable for an appreciably shorter time in 0·15 N NaCl. I think this is because, in sodium and potassium solutions, silver ions in the crystal lattice of the electrode surface are gradually replaced by the other cations, and this changes the electrodes' E_0. The effect would be expected to increase with concentration. In HCl there would be no such ions available.

I have made silver chloride electrodes by electrodeposition on platinum wire, sealed into glass or polythene. Such electrodes come to temperature equilibrium in five or ten minutes: very much sooner than the type made from spongy silver oxide; and they can be stripped and replated as often as necessary, which is not true of a silver wire. To get reproducible electrode potentials on different occasions the conditions of electrolyte and current density must be carefully controlled, but this becomes a routine. The whole process of stripping and replating takes about 45 minutes.

Usually, a set of six similar electrodes mounted in the same rubber bung are all plated simultaneously. Ten minutes after replacing them in their electrode vessel in the water bath, the potential difference between them is measured. Usually all six will agree to within $\pm$ 25 microvolts, but sometimes one is off by 100 or 200 microvolts. In N/10 NaCl at 37°C. these differences slowly increase over the next week or two. The set is replated when there are no longer three which agree within $\pm$ 100 microvolts. This is not strictly necessary, however, since for many weeks the rate of drift is small enough to take a series of readings over an hour or two.

The same considerations apply to the reference electrode

within the glass electrode. In the usual design of bulb electrode they are far from being properly satisfied, and I have found that their faults are the most usual cause of poor performance in commercial electrodes. Their troubles are two: the wire is only partly immersed in the hydrochloric acid; and when the electrode is used in a waterbath, only part of the wire is kept at constant temperature, the shank of the electrode being out in the air. This last fault does not affect apparatus kept at room temperature, but in a bath at 37°C. it can cause drifts in electrode potential of up to 2 millivolts in an hour. Finally, the wire turns from brown to white, either patchily, or all over, and the electrode potential becomes most unpredictable. These troubles are completely cured by cutting off the top of the electrode, and replacing the wire by a suitably designed reference electrode. I have made these by sealing a short length of platinum wire into a polythene rod machined to be a good fit in the shank of the glass electrode. The new reference electrode sits well down in the glass bulb, completely covered by the HCl, even if the electrode is tipped up, and is well within that part of the electrode kept at constant temperature by the test solution.

(3) Choice of Reference Solutions

Saturated KCl is most often used, because it reduces the size of junction potentials. But it will precipitate proteins, and perhaps for this reason it does not make so stable or reproducible a junction with blood. Isotonic NaCl is better in this respect, and so is N/10 NaCl, which I have used because it suits my electrodes. N/10 NaCl, though not isotonic, is equimolar in chloride with plasma, and this will tend to stabilize junction potentials.

Liquid Junctions. Liquid junctions may be of two kinds: flowing, or static. Flowing junctions are usually considered to give the most reproducible results, and figures reported for them have been within $\pm$ 20 microvolts. But they are not of much use for measurements in blood, because of the size of the sample needed, and the difficulty in maintaining anaerobic conditions.

When static junctions are considered, their variability may be analysed in two parts: the reproducibility of the potential when the junction is first made, and its drift with time after-wards. In general, the reproducibility of the junction depends on the two liquid surfaces being brought together in exactly the same way on each occasion. The subsequent drift is caused by the diffusion of the two electrolytes into each other.

Rigid mathematical analysis of the expected behaviour of any given arrangement is seldom possible, but there are three special sets of conditions under which their behaviour is simplified.

(1) If the two solutions contain the same electrolyte at different concentrations, then the junction potential should be independent of the mechanical form of the junction, and of time.

(2) If the two solutions contain an ion in common, at the same concentration in each, the variable factors in passing through the junction are reduced.

(3) If the junction is so arranged that when the solutions diffuse into each other, the distribution of the ions can main-tain an axial symmetry around a line perpendicular to the plane of the junction, then it appears that the potential should be independent of time while this condition is maintained, regardless of the nature of the two electrolytes.

An approximation may be made to one of the first two conditions for junctions with blood, by using either $0.15 N$ or $0.1 N$ sodium chloride as reference solution.

The last condition is the most important when solutions of all kinds are considered. If a junction is designed to be mechanically rigid and reproducible, and also to maintain the axial symmetry of the diffusing ions, then its potential should be reproducible, and free from drift.

There are a number of standard devices for making liquid junctions, such as ground glass sleeves, sintered discs and junctions round tap barrels, but they do not really make the junction in exactly the same way each time. They were all found to give potentials which varied by about ± 0.2 milli-volts, and were not free from drift. The best of them was formed by an agar plug in the end of a tube which had been drawn out to capillary size, and bent up in a hook. This gave potentials varying by ± 0.1 millivolt, and makes a useful kind of dip electrode.

But static junctions of the capillary type, where the two solutions are brought directly into contact, can give better results than this. The junction described below and illustrated in Fig. 1 was made to satisfy as closely as possible the two conditions suggested.

The junction is made between 1 mm. diameter tubes formed by holes drilled at right angles to flat ground surfaces of pieces of perspex rod. The tubes proper are at the centre of the rod. The two ground surfaces slide over each other, with a smear of silicone grease. Each side also bears an eccentric hole so placed that in one position both central holes will meet their opposite eccentric holes. In this position the two tubes are flushed through with their respective electrolytes, and then slid across until the central holes coincide. Thus two sharply cut off liquid surfaces are brought into contact. Direct flow of fluid through the junction is prevented by a wide bore stopcock on the reference fluid side, which allows ionic conduction round its bore.

This arrangement has proved an extremely satisfactory and versatile form of junction, which can be connected to a wide range of electrode systems, both capillary and of the normal type, by means of 1 mm. polythene tubing. The junction potentials are usually reproducible to within $\pm$ 30 microvolts, and the drift with time is very small. It is often only 100 microvolts when left overnight.

Wynn and Ludbrook's (1957) electrode system for blood measurements also achieves rigidity, and a certain degree of axial symmetry, by the shape of the glass electrode and its vessel. The bringing together of the two fluids is perhaps not quite so satisfactory, but its performance appears to be very good.

A very simple and useful form of junction, though not so reproducible, is made by dipping the end of a 1 mm. polythene tube directly into the test fluid. This arrangement provides a nice confirmation of the importance of axial symmetry. If the end of the tube is well in the middle of the fluid, the potential is usually reproducible to $\pm$ 100 microvolts, and drift may be 200 microvolts in an hour. But if the tube lies against the side of the vessel, the drift is increased by three or four times. A different kind of stability is provided if the test solution is

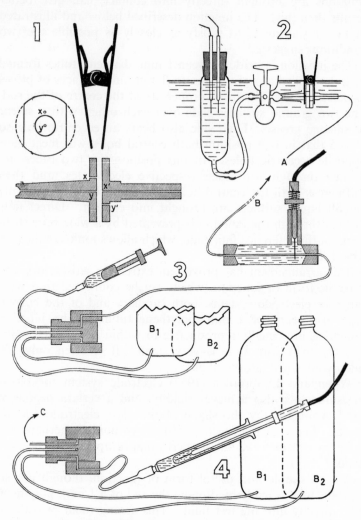

The sliding liquid junction, and two ways of using it.

stirred vigorously the whole time. Presumably then the fluid outside the tube is constantly renewed. The potential is usually constant to within $\pm$ 100 microvolts. This arrangement is useful for potentiometric titrations.

Glass Electrodes. Probably the best theory of the action of the glass electrode is to consider the glass as a membrane through which only the most mobile ions, hydrogen ions, can migrate. Each of its surfaces can then be considered as a hydrogen electrode, and the total potential difference across the membrane will vary directly as the difference in pH between the solutions on either side. The two surfaces are connected by the glass, which acts only as a high resistance. Unfortunately, the Eo's for the two surfaces are never identical, and this produces a residual asymmetry potential.

Almost all the details of the behaviour of glass electrodes can be predicted correctly from this theory. A notable exception in the departure from a linear pH/E.M.F. relation at high pH. This may be explained if the membrane is not entirely impermeable to other ions, and in particular to sodium ions.

FIG. 1 shows details of the junction. The two halves are turned from 1 in. perspex rod. The opposing surfaces are ground flat, and greased with silicone grease. They are kept together by a " Quickfit " spherical joint clip, and when clipped will slide over each other. The shank of one side is turned to a B10 cone, to fit the B10 socket on the stopcock shown in Fig. 2. The central hole is 1 mm. diameter and takes a No. 1 polythene tube as a push fit. These joints are satisfactory when greased with silicone grease. The eccentric holes X, and Y' are so placed that when X coincides with X', then Y coincides with Y'. In this position, fluid from each side is flushed through. Then flow is stopped by the stopcock, and the two halves slid across, bringing the two sharply cut-off liquid surfaces at Y and X' into contact.

FIG. 2 shows the junction connected to the reference half-cell by a wide-bore stopcock, which stops liquid flow without breaking the electrical pathway. A may be connected either to B, or C, below, by a polythene tube.

FIG. 3. The connection passes through a capillary glass electrode to a three-way tap. One way is connected to a syringe containing the unknown sample; the other two to polythene bottles of standard buffer. The electrode and junction may thus be filled and washed through with each fluid in turn.

FIG. 4. An E.I.L. Syringe electrode is connected to the three-way tap. One way goes to the junction; the other two to the standard buffers. The syringe is connected up containing the unknown sample, and a reading taken. By manipulating the tap, it may then be emptied through the junction, and refilled with buffer without being lifted from the water-baths.

The electrode potential will then be partly controlled by the concentration of these ions.

In particular, the theory suggests that the conditions for stable potentials will be the same as those for a reference electrode, i.e.

(*a*) The surface must be stable and uniform.

(*b*) Both sides must be completely immersed in electrolyte.

(*c*) It must be kept at constant temperature.

This last condition was found to be most important when a reproducibility better than $\pm$ 0·2 millivolts was sought. When an electrode was lifted from one solution to another, each in a beaker in the waterbath at 37°C., the cooling and reheating which occurred in these few seconds appeared to produce a change in the asymmetry potential, so that the electrode might never return to the original potential when it was put back into the first solution. Using this method, reproducibility of the potentials obtained by alternating between two buffers was never better than $\pm$ 0·2 millivolts; and frequent changes tended to produce a cumulative drift in asymmetry potential. But when an electrode system was designed in which the solution could be changed while always keeping the glass surface immersed in fluid at constant temperature, then the reproducibility between two buffers immediately improved, until it seemed to be controlled not by the glass electrode, but by the junction and the reference electrodes.

It is not at all easy to design such an electrode chamber for measurements on small volumes of unknown fluid, because the chamber cannot be emptied, dried, and refilled. When chambers of very small volume were made for the usual type of bulb electrode giving through flow to the liquid junction, the importance of the second condition became obvious. Such chambers have an irregular shape round the root of the glass bulb; it is very difficult to change solutions without admitting small air bubbles, which are difficult to dislodge from the surface of the electrode. If such bubbles remain they always produce abnormal and drifting potentials.

So far, I have been successful with two different electrode systems. One is the syringe electrode produced by E.I.L. (Fig. 4). When its inner chloride electrode is suitably modified, the electrode itself is of remarkably low resistance and very nice to use. For measurements, the syringe fits a Luer socket on the end of a 1·5 mm. polythene tube, which leads to a three-way tap, made of perspex, immersed in the bath. One arm of the tap passes to the liquid junction, and the other two to reservoirs of standard buffer in the bath. Blood is taken from the patient into the syringe and the syringe is fitted to its tube and suspended in the bath. Blood is expelled through the tap to make the liquid junction, and readings are taken. Then, by turning the tap, the syringe is rinsed out with buffer, and standardizing readings are taken. It is important to note that no less than twelve rinsings are required. With this system consecutive fillings of the same buffer give readings within $\pm$ 0·1 millivolts. When alternating between two buffers, repeatability is not so good, but in a long series the standard deviation was 0·1 millivolts, and all lay within $\pm$ 0·2 millivolts.

This, then, is the probable accuracy of blood pH measurements by this method.

The other system employed a capillary electrode (Fig. 2). The capillary was embedded in a perspex outer case, and the space between the two filled with $N/10$ HCl, containing a reference electrode. The two ends of the capillary were connected to polythene tubes; one direct to the liquid junction, and the other to the four-way tap. Any syringe containing a blood sample could be plugged in to the Luer socket, and the sample passed through the tap to fill the capillary and junction. Buffer readings are taken by turning the tap.

This system looks like being the best yet. Four or five readings can be taken on a 1 cc. sample: the sample comes quickly to temperature equilibrium in passing through the thin tubing in the bath; rinsing of the capillary is quickly complete, and bubbles are swept straight through it. With the best of my capillary electrodes the reproducibility between two buffers was within $\pm$ 50 microvolts, but the construction of capillary electrodes is still very tricky, and not all are as good as this.

REFERENCES

HILLS, G. J., and IVES, D. J. G. (1951). The Hydrogen-Calomel Cell. *J. chem. Soc.*, **1**, 305.
WYNN, V., and LUDBROOK, J. (1957). A Method of Measuring the pH of Body-fluids. *Lancet*, **1**, 1068.

DISCUSSION

Mattock: I find these results of Dr. Wright's very interesting. I must confess I have had prior notice of them and have had a lot of discussion with Dr. Wright, so it is rather artificial for me to bring up some of the points I have already raised with him. Concerning his reference to the stability of commercial calomel electrodes, I think he may have been a little unfortunate. There are other electrode manufacturers here; I am sure they will bear me out on the question of the degree of stability achievable—but it does depend very much on maintaining absolute thermal stability. Our work was done with a liquid junction of the ceramic plug type. We have done a lot of work on ceramic plugs and on ground glass sleeves and we find that ground glass sleeves are definitely inferior. With ceramic plugs we have obtained the overall reproducibility figure of about $\pm \cdot 1$ of a millivolt. (I have some statistical figures obtained with solutions of different pH values. Reproducibility does depend on pH to a very large extent.) The other point Dr. Wright made is, I think, a very important one: the fact that you get a certain amount of instability from your glass electrode with plain silver chloride wire dipping into the inner solution is highly significant: I am quite sure (and Dr. Wright has expressed this opinion to me himself) that it is due to surface oxidation at the air-liquid interface causing drift. From a manufacturing point of view the possibility of achieving consistent reproducibility in general production is rather difficult, because we have ourselves obtained highly reproducible electrodes and others not so reproducible; Dr. Wright seems to have found some of those. There is one other point I would like to make: Dr. Wright says that high resistance electrodes take a long time to reach equilibrium which may be due to the " ionization current ". I think it is more likely to be due to a resistance-capacity effect, but that is a small feature. I have very few comments apart from this because I am essentially in agreement with everything Dr. Wright says. He has done a very fine job in analysing some of the pure measurement problems.

Lauchlan: I think that one of the most useful things Dr. Wright should consider is what will be the effect of leakage either by the valve or the leads. So many people try and modify their electrode systems, break open the caps, reconnect them and then write in to say the electrode is no good. They will never realize that a dirty finger will make virtually a short circuit in the glass electrode. It is most valuable that the point is being well brought out. Concerning reference electrodes, has Dr. Wright tried the addition of silver chloride to potassium chloride to prevent further solution of the silver chloride from the electrode itself?

Wright: I have, but I have never been very successful with it.

Lauchlan: In making measurements to such a fine degree of accuracy I think there is a danger of traces of H_2S from some of the bungs that are used lightheartedly in silver chloride electrode systems. Some of the bungs seem all right: others seem to give off large quantities of H_2S with the greatest of ease. I think some of the drifts on the glass electrode itself are due to the gradual solution of the glass inside the bulb. As the electrode is moved about so the liquid is stirred up inside and the glass is slowly dissolving. I have examined an electrode which has been kept for a number of years and have been watching the potential going slowly down and down and down, and finally I opened it up and found it had an alkali inside and not an acid. It is easy to imagine what is happening if you are measuring to a few microvolts. Frankly, I was sorry to see Agar bridges arriving again. I had hoped we had buried them. The usual snag with these is that when least expected the gel comes loose from the glass and there is a flushing of liquid, just before an experiment. The initial drift may be due to change of hydration of the glass. In transferring the electrode from one solution to another, you dry it. Here you upset the hydration condition of the glass electrode in that period and therefore it must take a few seconds to settle down.

Mattock: Dr. Wright made a very interesting point which I am sure many gentlemen who have measured pH to any degree of accuracy, particularly with blood, must have noticed: that is, a lack of correlation between theoretical potential and the observed one in terms of the Nernst equation relationship. Mr. Ludbrook in fact observed a deviation of, I think, something of the order of 2 millivolts, wasn't it?

Ludbrook: Yes; 1 millivolt.

Mattock: Of the order of 1 or 2 millivolts in 60. Now, I am quite certain this is not due to electrical leakage, and it is not due to a pH effect on the liquid junction—the magnitude is far too large. Having observed something rather similar with certain glasses myself, I have come to the conclusion that it is an asymmetry potential effect, due to a change in pH going from one buffer to another; it is a function to some extent of the shape of the glass electrode and also its thickness. Some years ago at the National Bureau of Standards, it was found that the apparent scale length was affected by changes in the thickness of the glass electrode and to a certain extent by the shape. We have confirmed this ourselves and with some of the smaller glass electrodes which are used in blood pH measurement one could quite easily get this sort of problem. I think asymmetry potential is something which can be recognized, but at the same time has to be distinguished from the slow poisoning which seems to occur in glass electrodes as a result of deposition and which causes a very marked drift, not 58 instead of 60, but 47 instead of 60, which I think Dr. Nunn has observed. That is definitely poisoning of the glass and can sometimes be removed. I think that various people here will have experienced this and I would like to hear if they have anything to say about it.

Wynn: Dr. Mattock has brought up an important and interesting point. Since Mr. Ludbrook and I published our paper on the method of blood pH measurement, I occasionally get requests from various people to check the pH of their buffer solutions for them because they cannot make the pH they observe agree with the theoretical pH. When I come to test the pH of the buffer I usually find it agrees closely with buffer made up in my own laboratory. I suspect that the reason for the difficulty is, as Dr. Mattock has just said, and as Dr. Wright mentioned, that the response of the glass electrode is not exactly the theoretical response in every glass electrode tested. It varies, whereas a pH meter has a fixed scale. I think that Dr. Wright said that measurements should be in millivolt measurements, and not made in terms of pH, and with this I wholeheartedly agree. In response to Dr. Wright's paper, which I enjoyed very much, there are a number of practical points. I agree that the theoretical approach to this problem is tremendously important. The immediate practical issue, however, is to what degree of accuracy do we wish to measure blood pH? Having decided upon this point, the next question is what degree of stability do we require? Because accuracy and stability are not the same thing. I would say, roughly speaking, that if we could measure blood pH reproducibly to 0·01 pH, that is to say, about $\frac{1}{2}$ millivolt, that would be good enough for most clinical applications. I think that preferably the whole system of measurement should be stable for at least 1 hour.

Ludbrook: May I raise two small points? First, the millivolt-pH ratio of glass electrodes. We noticed when doing this work that an individual glass electrode kept the same ratio for some months, though there was considerable variation in the ratio for different electrodes. I don't know whether this has been a common experience. Secondly, may I make a plea to the makers of direct reading pH apparatus to provide an adjustor to allow for the millivolt-pH ratio of the glass electrode actually in use, and either dispense with the temperature compensator or combine the two? If one is to read pH rather than millivolts on a dial the conversion factor is all important to the accuracy of the instrument.

IV. ELECTROCHEMICAL ASPECTS OF BLOOD pH MEASUREMENTS

G. Mattock

Electronic Instruments Ltd., Richmond, Surrey

The Theoretical Basis of pH[1]

Although it is possible to define pH in various ways, as by equating it with $- \log c_{H^+}$ or with $- \log a_{H^+}$, where c_{H^+} and a_{H^+} are the concentration and activity* of hydrogen ions in a solution, respectively, there are theoretical limitations to the extent to which the definitions may be realized in practice. It is not possible to measure individual ion activities by any known thermodynamic means; any attempt to measure pH $= - \log a_{H^+}$ inevitably involves approximations, and the source and magnitude of the uncertainty will depend on the actual experimental system. Thus the use of different systems can give rise to different " pH " values for the same solution.

Two types of electrochemical cell may be used, from which an E.M.F. value may be obtained to relate to pH.

(i) In a cell without liquid junction, such as

$$Pt; H_2 \mid buffer, Cl^- \mid AgCl; Ag,$$

the two electrodes are in reversible equilibrium with the contained solution, with an E.M.F., E, given by

$$E = E^\circ + \frac{2 \cdot 3026RT}{F} (\log a_{H^+} + \log a_{Cl^-})$$

(R is the gas constant, T is the absolute temperature, and F is the Faraday). If the pH of the contained solution is to be defined solely in terms of a_{H^+}, a value for the individual ion activity, a_{Cl^-}, must be *assumed*.

(ii) A more common cell employs a liquid junction, as with

$$Pt; H_2 \mid buffer \parallel salt\ bridge \parallel reference\ electrode,$$

---

* Concentrations and activities are related by an " activity coefficient ", f, such that
$$a = cf$$
Nearly all colligative properties of solutions are a function of activities, rather than concentrations.

where the E.M.F. expression

$$E = E^{\circ} + \frac{2 \cdot 3026 RT}{F} \log a_{H^+} + E_j - E_{ref.}$$

incorporates a " liquid junction potential " term, E_j, which is both non-calculable and variable. ($E_{ref.}$ is the E.M.F. of the reference electrode.) Any pH found with such a cell will include the liquid junction potential term, unless an attempt is made to eliminate it (although it must be emphasized that elimination cannot be achieved with certainty).

pH as an Estimate of Acid-Base Ratios

If the pH values of a series of solutions are defined on the basis of any given cell system, some estimate of the uncertainty in obtaining $pH = - \log a_{H^+}$ can often be made. However, if a completely different solution is measured by calibration of the cell system with the defined solutions, an extra uncertainty can be built into the observation; as, for example, would occur when the unknown solution caused a marked change in E_j (undoubtedly the case with blood). In medical work, however, it is usually concentrations that are sought (although in some cases activities would undoubtedly be more relevant).

The pH constitutes an assessment of the acid-base ratio of a solution. This is expressed in the familiar Henderson-Hasselbach equation, written precisely for an acid-base equilibrium of

$$HA \rightleftharpoons H^+ + A^-$$

as

$$pH = - \log a_{H^+} = - \log K + \log \frac{a_{A^-}}{a_{HA}}$$

where $K = \dfrac{a_{H^+} \cdot a_{A^-}}{a_{HA}}$. With $pK = - \log K$,

$$pH = pK + \log \frac{a_{A^-}}{a_{HA}} = pK + \log \frac{f_{A^-}}{f_{HA}} + \log \frac{c_{A^-}}{c_{HA}}$$

$$= pK' + \log \frac{c_{A^-}}{c_{HA}}$$

Here, K' is the " concentration " or " classical " dissociation constant. K is a true constant for a given temperature; but K' can be changed by changes in $\dfrac{f_{A^-}}{f_{HA}}$, as well as by experimental artifacts such as variations in the conditions causing a change in E_j, for example, if pK' is measured using a cell with liquid junction.

If $\log \frac{c_{A^-}}{c_{HA}}$ is to be found from a pH measurement, a value of pK' must be assumed. Quite apart from the factors already mentioned, this value will depend on the pH values assumed for the standardizing buffers used in the original determination of pK'. It is clearly necessary to use the same cell system and buffers for the pH measurement on the unknown as used in the evaluation of pK'. Thus if the original Sørensen buffers were used to find pK', but a more modern series were used to calibrate for sample pH measurement, an error of 0·04 pH unit could be incorporated, corresponding to 9 per cent error in the determination of $\frac{c_{A^-}}{c_{HA}}$. An alternative technique, used by Astrup,[2] involves interpolation on a plot of measured pH against known $\log \frac{c_{A^-}}{c_{HA}}$. In this case a knowledge of pK' is not necessary, the only requirement being constancy in pK' over the range of conditions employed. The Jørgensen-Astrup blood bicarbonate determination method,[3] however, demands a knowledge of pK' (and also of α, the carbon dioxide solubility coefficient), and it is worth noting that Sørensen buffers were employed in the original work assuming pK' = 6·11 at 38° C. for blood. The use of differently defined buffers and the same pK' value could easily give rise to significant variations. Severinghaus et al.[4] have quoted pK' values determined with reference to buffers having values assigned by the National Bureau of Standards (U.S.A.).

The Characteristics of pH Scales

The pH values found by any given method for a series of solutions constitute a " pH scale ". From the preceding remarks, it is obviously highly desirable that all workers employ the same scale, if consistency and comparison are to be possible. Such a scale should be internationally acceptable, and include pH values defined to a discrimination level that is at least consistent with the discrimination experimentally achievable.

It is useful to summarize the features of those pH scales which have had the widest application (see Table 1 for data):

(a) **Sørensen Scale.** [1a] This was originally defined in terms of c_{H^+}, on the basis of certain assumptions regarding the dissociation of acids that are no longer considered true, and an attempt was made to eliminate E_j by an extrapolation technique. It has been widely used in blood pH investigations (e.g. by Astrup), but suffers from the considerable disadvantage that it gives buffer pH values which are about 0·04 pH unit different from other current widely used scales. Furthermore, values are only presented to 0·01 pH unit, and modern techniques with the glass electrode probably permit of a better discrimination. Although theoretical significance of the pH scale is not particularly important in the present context, the highly dubious basis of the Sørensen scale certainly does not recommend its perpetuation.

(b) **Hitchcock-Taylor**[5] and **MacInnes-Belcher-Shedlovsky Scales.**[6] These are based on measurements with cells incorporating a liquid junction, and differ primarily in the extrapolation details concerning the attempt to eliminate the liquid junction potential. The MacInnes scale seems to have little value for physiological work, since its range of buffers is too restricted. The Hitchcock-Taylor system has been used by Wynn and Ludbrook,[7] on account of the finer discrimination of its defined values; although it may be noted that Hitchcock and Taylor themselves have recommended a rounding-off of the values to 0·005 pH unit.

(c) **National Bureau of Standards (U.S.A.) Scale.**[8] Probably the most extensive investigation on the subject of pH scales has been carried out by workers at the N.B.S. during the years following the war, and the result has been a scale defined in terms of cells without liquid junction of the type already mentioned. Individual ion activities have been calculated from theoretical equations, and the scale is considered theoretically significant to within $\pm$ 0·01 pH unit.

(d) **British Standards Scale.**[9] In contrast to all the other scales, no attempt has been made to relate pH with a theoretical quantity. A solution of 0·05 M potassium hydrogen phthalate is defined as having a pH of 4·000 exactly at 15° C., and all other values, including those of unknown samples, are related to this primary standard. Secondary buffer values are based on the work of several different investigators, with agreement to not better than 0·01 pH unit: one buffer solution is in fact quoted with two values at 38° C. (see Table 1).

TABLE 1. *Comparison Between Different pH Scales at 38° C.*

Buffer Solution	Hitchcock-Taylor	MacInnes-Belcher-Shedlovsky	N.B.S. (inter-polated)	B.S.
0·05 M potassium hydrogen phthalate	4·025	4·015	4·03	4·026
0·1 M acetic acid; 0·1 M sodium acetate	4·655	4·635	—	4·65 or 4·66
0·025 M potassium dihydrogen phosphate; 0·025 M disodium hydrogen phosphate	6·835	—	6·84	6·84
0·01 M borax	—	—	9·08	—
0·05 M borax	9·070	—	(9·09)	9·07

Sørensen buffers are based on a scale whose E° reference value is ~ 0·04 pH unit different from those above, so that pH ≅ pH (Sørensen) + 0·04.

Choice of a pH Scale

It seems advisable to adopt a system that is already widely used, for which there is a maximum of experimental data available, and which incorporates an appropriate degree of numerical discrimination in its buffer pH values. All the scales so far defined have limitations in the present context, but the considerable amount of work already carried out by workers at the National Bureau of Standards merits examination, since it is the basis of the N.B.S. scale so widely used in the U.K. as well as the U.S.A.

The N.B.S. scale itself, like the B.S. scale, is proposed to a fineness of 0·01 pH unit, which seems a little inadequate in view of the discrimination which has apparently been achieved in recent work on glass electrode systems. Wynn and Ludbrook[7] reported 0·0025 pH unit standard deviation in a run of twelve measurements on an approximately 7·3 pH buffer following standardization in 6·835 pH phosphate buffer, which corresponds to a reproducibility of $\pm$ 0·005 pH unit. Wright (personal communication) has obtained $\pm$ 0·002 pH reproducibility with observation on one buffer; measurement of a borax solution, following phthalate standardization, gave a reproducibility of $\pm$ 0·004 pH unit. It is probably true to say that the level more generally to be expected in routine measurements would be $\pm$ 0·005 $-$ 0·01 pH unit, but it is obviously important to cater for possibilities of improvements in experimental techniques.

In the original studies on which the N.B.S. scale is based, pH values for the buffer solutions were calculated to the third decimal place, on the assumption of reasonable values for an ionic radius parameter. The limitation subsequently applied to the scale of 0·01 unit reflects the caution felt in regard to the theoretical limitations; but with empirical measurements as are being discussed here, such considerations are not so important. It seems reasonable to adopt the values given in the original papers, thus obtaining the appropriate degree of fineness while retaining consistency with the N.B.S. scale proper. The availability of the data renders unnecessary the addition of arbitrary zeros to the N.B.S. scale values.

The equimolar 0·025 M phosphate buffer solution is an obvious choice as the primary standard, in view of the fact that its pH is closest of the standard buffers to blood pH. Cell systems require calibration by observation of the pH of a second buffer following standardization with the primary solution; borax is suitable here, since the blood pH range is then straddled. One practical disadvantage of the N.B.S. borate solution here becomes evident: that its dilution (0·01 M) renders its buffer properties poorer than are really desirable in a standard. The atmospheric absorption of as little as 0·2 per cent of carbon dioxide can lower the pH by 0·001 unit [1b]. For this reason the 0·05 M solution is preferable (and is in fact used in the British Standard scale). Data are available from the same (N.B.S.) sources for this solution, so there appears no reason why it should not be adopted. In the 35°– 40° C. region, the pH differences between the 0·01 M and 0·05 M solutions are within 0·01 unit. A third buffer is useful for checks on cell performance: here the phthalate solution seems suitable.

TABLE 2. *A Suggested pH Scale for Standardization of Cell Assemblies for Blood pH Measurements*

The primary standard is the phosphate buffer.
The data given at 5° C. intervals, starting at 0° C., are derived from references given below; intermediate figures have been obtained by interpolation.

Temperature ° C.	0·05 M potassium hydrogen phthalate (ref. 8a)	0·025 M disodium hydrogen phosphate; 0·025 M potassium dihydrogen phosphate (ref. 8b)	0·05 M sodium tetraborate decahydrate (ref.8c)
0	4·012	6·983	9·512
1	4·010	6·976	9·496
2	4·009	6·969	9·480
3	4·007	6·961	9·464
4	4·006	6·956	9·449
5	4·005	6·950	9·434
6	4·004	6·944	9·419
7	4·003	6·938	9·404
8	4·002	6·933	9·389
9	4·002	6·927	9·375
10	4·001	6·922	9·362
11	4·001	6·916	9·350
12	4·000	6·911	9·338
13	4·000	6·906	9·326
14	4·000	6·901	9·315
15	4·000	6·896	9·305
16	4·000	6·892	9·294
17	4·000	6·888	9·282
18	4·000	6·885	9·270
19	4·001	6·881	9·259
20	4·001	6·878	9·247
21	4·002	6·874	9·236
22	4·002	6·870	9·226
23	4·003	6·867	9·216
24	4·004	6·863	9·206
25	4·005	6·860	9·196
26	4·006	6·857	9·187
27	4·007	6·855	9·178
28	4·008	6·853	9·169
29	4·010	6·851	9·161
30	4·011	6·849	9·152
31	4·012	6·847	9·143
32	4·014	6·846	9·134
33	4·015	6·844	9·126
34	4·017	6·843	9·117
35	4·019	6·842	9·109
36	4·021	6·841	9·101
37	4·023	6·840	9·093
38	4·025	6·839	9·085
39	4·027	6·838	9·077
40	4·030	6·837	9·069
41	4·032	6·837	9·062
42	4·035	6·836	9·055
43	4·038	6·835	9·049
44	4·040	6·834	9·043
45	4·043	6·834	9·037
46	4·046	6·834	9·031
47	4·049	6·833	9·025
48	4·052	6·833	9·019
49	4·055	6·833	9·013
50	4·059	6·833	9·008

In Table 2, the suggested pH values are quoted.* The original sources provide data at 5° C. intervals; interpolation gives values for 1° C. intervals.

It must be borne in mind that the N.B.S. solutions have been studied in cells without liquid junction. Where a cell with liquid junction is used, some deviation from the slope expected from the phosphate-borate values may ensue, from the introduction of a pH-dependent liquid junction potential. Bates, Pinching and Smith [8a] have studied the effects of liquid junction potentials at 25° C. by comparing observed pH values with those obtained from cells without liquid junction, referred to a standardization with the phosphate solution. The results suggest that the deviation with 0·01 M borax may be of the order of 0·003 pH unit; which would mean a correction factor of only ~ 0·001 pH unit in the blood pH range, which is experimentally negligible. In fact, only negligible error would ensue if the borate and phthalate pH values were rounded off to 0·005 pH unit. A closer definition of the primary phosphate standard would still be required, however.

An alternative scheme would be to adopt the British Standard values for phosphate, phthalate and borate, adding an arbitrary third figure of zero where only two decimal place figures are given in the Standard. The drawback with B.S. 1647 as it at present stands is that values for the phosphate and borate buffers are only given for 25° C. and 38° C.; this does not really permit easy interpolation, particularly for the temperature-sensitive borate, or extrapolation to regions above 38° C. This is not to say that it could not be utilized, but it seems sounder to employ the data already available from work forming the basis of the more widely used N.B.S. scale.

It would be possible, of course, to establish a value for borate and any other buffer in a cell with liquid junction, by executing a comprehensive series of carefully planned experiments. It may be felt that this is desirable, along with the establishment of a convenient secondary buffer of pH intermediate between phosphate and borate. The execution of

---

* The original N.B.S. work was carried out using molalities rather than molarities. The error from the use of molarities is probably negligible, and the convenience of a molarity scale commends its use.

such an investigation would preferably be spread among several groups of workers under the sponsorship of an internationally recognized body. The present symposium offers an excellent opportunity for an exchange of views on the merits or otherwise of initiating an extensive experimental programme. It is perhaps appropriate to point out, however, that it is by no means certain that further experimental work would result in phosphate and borate data more than marginally better for the present purposes than those already available; perhaps a more valuable contribution would be the definition of a buffer of pH between 7·2 and 7·5 that is consistent with the scale recommended here.

Use of a Chosen pH Scale

Certain practical aspects in the use of a pH scale remain for consideration.

(a) The stability and reproducibility of the standardizations depends on the buffers themselves as well as on the cell system employed. (Directions for preparation are given by Bates [1b].) Diffusion of electrolyte from the salt bridge can affect the pH of the buffer, and give drifting readings. Table 3 gives an idea of possible changes from the influence of added salt. This effect may be particularly noticeable where micro volumes of buffer are being used along with a saturated potassium chloride salt bridge.

TABLE 3. *Salt Effects on Buffers at 25° C.*
Δ pH = True pH — Observed pH.

Salt Concentration (in molarity)	Δ pH			
	0·05 M potassium hydrogen phthalate	0·025 M potassium dihydrogen phosphate; 0·025 M disodium hydrogen phosphate	0·01 M borax	0·05 M borax
	(+ KCl)	(+ NaCl)	(+NaCl)	(+NaCl)
0·01	0·01	0·01	0·01	0·00
0·02	0·02	0·02	0·01	0·01
0·03	0·03	0·03	0·02	0·01
0·05	0·05	0·05	0·04	0·02

(b) Saturated potassium chloride is the classical salt bridge solution. It has enjoyed wide application because of its effectiveness in reducing the magnitude of the liquid junction potential when in contact with electrolyte solutions. However, in blood pH measurements it suffers from the disadvantage that it causes coagulation, the process of which can probably lower the reproducibility and stability levels.

A more satisfactory alternative would be 0·15 M sodium chloride, which is virtually isotonic with blood, and which would reduce liquid junction problems from coagulation. The fact that it is not so efficient as saturated potassium chloride with buffers may be more than offset by a superior performance with blood. A highly suitable reference element would be the 0·15 M sodium chloride-calomel.

(c) For the results of different workers to be comparable, the type of cell to be used needs standardization. This follows from at least one consideration. A residual liquid junction potential, ΔE_j, being the difference between the E_j terms for the standardizing buffer and the sample, will be incorporated into all observations. The magnitude of ΔE_j depends on the type of salt bridge used (whether, e.g., 0·15 M sodium chloride or saturated potassium chloride) and on the sample, for a given buffer. It is worth noting that whole blood may produce quite different ΔE_j values from those occurring with plasma samples, from the presence of the suspended and colloidal matter giving rise to the " suspension effect " in whole blood. This factor alone could produce variations from one blood sample to another (depending on the condition of the samples), and probably accounts for the difference of 0·01 pH unit observed by Severinghaus *et al.*[10] between whole blood and plasma. Indeed, such variations could place a limitation on the generality of assumed pK values for whole blood, which by the method of their determination incorporate a ΔE_j term.

REFERENCES

1. For detailed discussions, see:
   (*a*) BATES, R. G. (1948). Definitions of pH Scales. *Chem. Rev.*, **42**, 1.
   (*b*) BATES, R. G. (1954). *Electrometric pH Determinations*. London, Chapman and Hall, chapters 2, 4 and 5.

(*c*) FELDMAN, I. (1956). Use and Abuse of pH Measurements. *Analyt. Chem.*, **28**, 1859.

(*d*) MATTOCK, G. (1957). The Accurate Measurement of pH. *Lab. Pract.*, **6**, 444.

2. ASTRUP, P. (1956). A Simple Electrometric Technique for the Determination of Carbon Dioxide Tension in Blood and Plasma, Total Content of Carbon Dioxide in Plasma, and Bicarbonate Content in " Separated " Plasma at a Fixed Carbon Dioxide Tension (40 mm. Hg). *Scand. J. clin. Lab. Invest.*, **8**, 33.

3. JØRGENSEN, K., and ASTRUP, P. (1957). Standard Bicarbonate, its Clinical Significance and a New Method for its Determination. *Scand. J. clin. Lab. Invest.*, **9**, 122.

4. SEVERINGHAUS, J. W., STUPFEL, M., and BRADLEY, A. F. (1956). Variations of Serum Carbonic Acid pK' with pH and Temperature. *J. appl. Physiol.*, **9**, 197.

5. HITCHCOCK, D. I., and TAYLOR, A. C. (1937). The Standardization of Hydrogen Ion Determinations. I. Hydrogen Electrode Measurements with a Liquid Junction. *J. Amer. chem. Soc.*, **59**, 1812, 2755. HITCHCOCK, D. I., and TAYLOR, A. C. (1938). II. A Standardization of the pH Scale at 38° C. *J. Amer. chem. Soc.*, **60**, 2710.

6. MACINNES, D. A., BELCHER, D., and SHEDLOVSKY, T. (1938). The Meaning and Standardization of the pH Scale. *J. Amer. chem. Soc.*, **60**, 1094.

7. WYNN, V., and LUDBROOK, J. (1957). A Method of Measuring the pH of Body Fluids. *Lancet*, i, 1068.

8. References 1(*a*) and 1(*b*) give details of most of the N.B.S. buffers; relevant to the present discussion are the following papers:

(*a*) HAMER, W. J., PINCHING, G. D., and ACREE, S. F. (1946). pH Standards at Various Temperatures: Aqueous Solutions of Acid Potassium Phthalate. *J. Res. Nat. Bur. Stand.*, **36**, 47.

(*b*) BATES, R. G., and ACREE, S. F. (1945). pH of Aqueous Mixtures of Potassium Dihydrogen Phosphate and Disodium Hydrogen Phosphate at 0° C. to 60° C. *J. Res. Nat. Bur. Stand.*, **34**, 373.

(*c*) MANOV, G. G., DELOLLIS, N. J., LINDVALL, P. W., and ACREE, S. F. (1946). Effect of Sodium Chloride on the Apparent Ionization Constant of Boric Acid and the pH Values of Borate Solutions. *J. Res. Nat. Bur. Stand.*, **36**, 543.

9. *pH Scale*, British Standard No. 1647, 1950.

10. SEVERINGHAUS, J. W., STUPFEL, M., and BRADLEY, A. F. (1956). Accuracy of Blood pH and P_{CO_2} Determinations. *J. appl. Physiol.*, **9**, 189.

DISCUSSION

Severinghaus: It is quite difficult to prepare phosphate buffer reproducibily and some people have had to work at it for a few months before they really got the technique. Now, this may have been their individual difficulty, but I have taken Dr. Bates's advice that he used the phthalate buffer which is so very stable that it never changes. One does not have to make it up so carefully. I would suggest that the phthalate really be considered the primary standard for another reason too, and this is because if you are going to measure the Δ E.M.F. over Δ pH for a glass electrode it is desirable to have a wide range. You like to be able to measure that between, let's say, 4 and 9 rather than around 7, and I think you get a little bit of additional accuracy in that measurement. And with regard to the borax, it certainly would be true that it could be ·05 pH units low from absorption of CO_2. I think the disadvantage of borax is the tendency to use it when old. It really ought to be made up freshly every time. So either one of those two is adequate. Thirdly I would like to suggest that in the scale which you submit for publication you include figures all the way down to 5° or 10° C., instead of just to 30° or 34°. Also in the definition of pK′ which one has to use to convert to P_{CO_2} from pH we have always felt that every investigator really ought to determine their own on the basis of tonometer experiments, or at least verify that the pK′ which they choose to use does, in fact, give them the right answer. Which is, in a sense, saying that they will be determining their own pK′. And I might at this point put on record the fact that the pK′ which we gave as an average is now known to be based on an incorrect solubility of CO_2 in plasma, because there are two solubility scales. One scale, taken from Van Slyke and Sendroy, is apparently based on dehydrated blood samples drawn from behind a tourniquet and having a low water content, so that the scale which gives the slightly higher solubility, which is found in Dill and Forbes in 1941 *American Journal of Physiology* is, in fact, the correct scale. And if one does use this solubility factor for CO_2, one should then use a pK′ of about 6·10 as is the standard.

Mattock: I will take first the point about the phthalate. Certainly the phthalate is stable, and in fact it has been adopted in the British Standard. I must say, personally, I have not had trouble with a phosphate buffer. I do not know what is the experience of Mr. Ludbrook, who has himself also used it; I can only speak from personal experience. It would have seemed to me perfectly satisfactory from many points of view. It is close to blood pH—as close as one can get within the buffer range of the accepted scales. On another point you made about the temperature range of pH values covered: the slide (Table 2) is not full for reasons of space. I have, in fact, interpolated values down to 20° C. and up to 50° C., but one can go down lower.* It is no problem, since it is all in the literature. I have merely interpolated rather carefully the data, so that it is easily available. All that is necessary is that everyone accepts the same interpolation, I feel. The pK point that you made—I am not quite clear—are you suggesting one should make a pK value for each blood sample?

Severinghaus: No. Empirically I would say that if you want to get the right P_{CO_2} from the pH, let's say, the best way to do it is to equilibrate blood, measure its pH and CO_2 content and—since you know the P_{CO_2}—calculate and see if you get the right answer.

* In fact, the table has now been extended to 0° C.—Ed.

If you do not, put in an arbitrary pK or some other factor which gives you the right answer, because with various electrode systems and various other laboratory techniques and perhaps errors in tonometry and all sorts of other things, it is better to prove your result than to assume it from somebody else's work. And as for the use of the phosphate versus the phthalate, I did not mean to imply that one would read blood against phthalate. For standardizing a system I have usually suggested that one use a secondary phosphate buffer in the pH range of blood, which one then standardizes at the beginning of using it, let's say once a month or once every six months—whatever it takes—against the phthalate and the borax buffers.

Mattock: But you will agree that it would be very helpful if such a buffer were mooted that there should be a general measure of agreement about the nature and pH value of the buffer as freshly made up, which would seem to merit some sort of investigation. I do not know who would undertake it, but it would certainly be a service to people who have to make a large number of measurements.

Severinghaus: To have a buffer of 7·2 or 7·4, you mean?

Mattock: Something of that order. Yes.

Severinghaus: Rather than the 6·86?

Mattock: Well, you would have your 6·86 buffer as the primary standard, but you would have this other one which you could put in quickly if you wanted to.

Severinghaus: We have always used these concentrates, as a matter of fact, and standardized them against a phthalate and a borax as often as need be and apparently every time you make them up you get the same pH, over the course of a year at least, and you can pick a concentrate which has a pH of 7.0 or 7.2.

Mattock: It is quite easy to get a value in that region. There is no sort of basic problem about that.

Campbell: Can I try to get a ruling on this from the experts, because there are a number of factors which can alter the voltage/pH relationship, is it not then desirable to use a buffer as close to blood as possible?

Mattock: I would say yes, definitely. From the general point of view anyway it is always true. I think everyone would agree with that.

Severinghaus: There is another reason for using buffer in the pH range of blood. If there is an error in the liquid junction it also is related to pH differences.

Mattock: Yes. Not only pH difference but in fact any sort of variant is a function of the difference between your buffer pH and your reading pH.

Severinghaus: There is another factor which might be mentioned here. It is most desirable to have a buffer which has about the same ionic concentration as blood, too. The liquid junction potential is also concentration dependent.

Mattock: It is certainly ionic strength dependent, but if you do that it is complicating the situation once more. You are adding sodium chloride, say, to your buffer to get the ionic strength level of your blood. You have then got to know the pH values of those new buffers, since the salt effect can be quite significant, as one of the slides (Table 3) showed.

Nunn: There are two points I should like to raise. Firstly, I am interested in the desirability of having a buffer closer to blood than 6·835. With a direct reading instrument of limited scale length, a buffer in the region of 7·4 would enable a higher sensitivity to be used and furthermore the effect of any error in the calibration of the glass electrode would be minimized. On the other hand, these advantages must be weighed against the undoubted stability of the Hitchcock-Taylor buffers. On two occasions we have compared our Hitchcock-Taylor buffers with those at St. Mary's Hospital. On each occasion we were unable to demonstrate any significant difference. Secondly, I should like to know the opinion of this symposium on the problem of which is more accurate—to measure blood pH at a fixed temperature (say, 38° C.), or at the patient's body temperature. In the first case the values of the buffers and the calibration factor of the glass electrode are accurately known, but one must assume a figure for the change of pH with temperature. For this purpose Rosenthal's data are widely used but he found a considerable scatter from one subject to another. Alternatively, if pH is measured at the patient's body temperature, it becomes necessary to calibrate the glass electrode for each patient and to obtain values for the pH of the buffer solutions over the range of body temperature which is expected. In addition the thermostat setting must be altered for each patient.

Mattock: From practical aspects it is obviously desirable to have your glass electrode at the same temperature both for buffer and for blood pH measurement for a number of reasons. The question of whether you are going to choose the same temperature as the body or a standard temperature is something which I am not qualified to discuss. I am sure there are several gentlemen here who have very strong views on it.

Campbell: Could I get a final ruling on this? If I followed Dr. Wright's paper and what Dr. Mattock was saying, I should have thought that the errors one may get from these factors are such that it is desirable, if one aims at 0·01 accuracy, that one should use a buffer within about 0·2 of the blood.

Brooks: I should like to confirm that I think the time has come for an internationally accepted buffer system, one which we can all accept, so that we can all measure pH with approximately the same factor within our pH systems. In other words, we measure the pH in our electrode system with its varying value and I think Dr. Severinghaus has suggested we overcome this difficulty of different electrode systems and possibly different buffer systems by taking the pK value for our own department. I think that is a possibility we ought to try. Perhaps however it would be better if we had an internationally accepted buffer system first.

Severinghaus: It certainly would be desirable to accept the pH standards and the gas tension standards, and then alter pK to fit.

Wynn: Before finishing this discussion about buffers, I would like to say that the phosphate and phthalate buffers which we use are kept in ordinary pyrex glassware without any preservative and are remarkably stable for months at a time. This is not true of most of the buffers we have tried in the 7·4 pH range. I think that as convenience is everything here, and accuracy not the most important consideration in clinical work, providing that we do not slip below a certain recognized standard, the phosphate 6·835 buffer seems to me to be quite adequate. It is theoretically possible that liquid junction potential changes might be slightly greater using such a buffer than if we were using 7·4 pH buffer in doing blood pH work. Finally, it is undesirable that commercial firms who sell buffers should certify a certain pH unless they can guarantee that the pH will remain unchanged under general handling conditions in a laboratory for many months. When we consider the potential harm which can come to a patient whose pH was wrongly measured because of a shift in the pH value of the buffer, and whose treatment was based upon such wrong measurements, the results can be disastrous.

Chairman: I think we might return to this very important question of standardization later on.

REFERENCE

DILL, D. B., and FORBES, W. H. (1941). Respiratory and Metabolic Effects of Hypothermia. *Amer. J. Physiol.*, **132,** 685.

V. ESTIMATION OF P_{CO_2} BY MEANS OF THE HENDERSON-HASSELBALCH EQUATION

John Ludbrook, M.B., F.R.C.S.

Norfolk and Norwich Hospital, Norwich

I WAS reluctant at first to speak on this subject before such distinguished and critical company, but finally persuaded myself that I might contrive to throw the Henderson-Hasselbalch equation, rather than myself, as a lamb among the wolves. I have very little which is new or original to say on this subject, but would like to take the opportunity of presenting to you some of the many problems associated with the use of this equation in determining P_{CO_2}, in the hope that we may between us in the following discussion be able to solve some of them, and perhaps be stimulated to solve the remainder.

The equation is, as you will know, derived from the law of mass action of Arrhenius and Ostwald. Henderson (1908b) applied the law to acid-base chemistry, and suggested its potential value in the quantitative study of the acid-base chemistry of living organisms. At the same time he grasped the concept of buffer action (Henderson, 1908a), and suggested the importance of the bicarbonate system as a blood buffer. He also pointed out that this system should be much more effective *in vivo* than *in vitro*, because of the ability of CO_2 to diffuse into or out of the system.

He wrote his equation as

$$[H^+] = k. \frac{[HA]}{[NaA]} \text{ (degree of dissociation of NaA)}$$

where k is the dissociation constant of the weak acid. In the same paper he suggested that k at 38° C. for a bicarbonate system should lie between 1 and 10×10^{-7}.

Hasselbalch (1916) rewrote the equation in terms of the concept of pH which Sørenson (1909) had introduced

$$pH = pK + p\delta + \log \frac{[NaHCO_3]}{[CO_2]}$$

where K is the first dissociation constant of H_2CO_3 and δ the degree of dissociation of $NaHCO_3$. He then incorporated pK and pδ into a single constant pK,' pδ being near to zero.

$$pH = pK' + \log \frac{[NaHCO_3]}{[CO_2]}$$

He went on to the experimental proof of the equation and obtained values of pK' at 38° C. of from 6·33 to 6·45.

Nowadays we write the working equation thus:

$$pH = pK' + \log \frac{[T_{CO_2} - a.P_{CO_2}]}{[a.P_{CO_2}]}$$

where T_{CO_2} = Total plasma CO_2 in m.moles/l.

P_{CO_2} = CO_2 tension in mm. Hg.

a = plasma CO_2 solubility factor in m.moles/mm. Hg/l.

pK' = composite constant including the first dissociation constant of H_2CO_3 and the activity coefficient of $NaHCO_3$.

We also assume that H_2CO_3 as such does not exist but is entirely in the form of dissolved CO_2. It would appear (Buytendyk *et al.*, 1927) that at physiological pH values at least 99 per cent of the CO_2 is dissolved and that the ratio H_2CO_3/ dissolved CO_2 is constant.

There is no doubt that even in a simple ionic aqueous system there are a lot of loopholes in this equation as a thermodynamic proposition, and of course its application to a plasma or blood system introduces further complications. However the fact is that it has been accepted as a useful and accurate equation by very good workers for a very long time. It is only recently, as methods of measuring pH have become more precise, and direct measurements of CO_2 tension have been introduced with a view to measuring alveolo-capillary gradients, that the accuracy of the use of the equation to calculate P_{CO_2} from pH and total plasma CO_2 measurements has been questioned.

There are two questions I should like to pose. Firstly, is the use of the equation in this way sufficiently accurate to be of value in applied physiological research? Secondly, is it sufficiently accurate for use in clinical medicine as a routine laboratory investigation?

There is no need to remind you that as well as the recent advances in respiratory physiology on the research side, there has been in post-war medicine an increasing recognition of the value of determinations of plasma pH, P_{CO_2} and HCO_3^- as a guide to the diagnosis and management of disturbances of acid-base balance, whether respiratory or metabolic. As these disturbances are comparatively common there are therefore increasing demands on the *routine* hospital laboratory to estimate these variables.

In order that we may have a clear basis for discussion, I propose to examine the equation and the factors affecting it step by step, in an attempt to quantitate the errors involved.

(i) Temperature

It is an extraordinary fact that no two groups of workers are decided as to what temperature should be used for the pH measurement, other than that it should be " body temperature " rather than " room temperature ". On reflection this is perhaps not so extraordinary, for of course the term " body temperature " is without meaning, as there is not only a diurnal variation in the individual, and a scatter between individuals, but temperature gradients throughout the tissues of the body. It is true that if one wishes to measure the alveolo-capillary gradient of P_{CO_2} the two measurements of P_{CO_2} must be made at the same temperature. It is equally obvious that one cannot use the *actual* temperature existing at the site of the gradient. However, provided both measurements are made at the same temperature, and this is close to that at the site, there is an insignificant error involved. We should therefore, I believe, agree on a temperature at which to make and express our measurements of pH and P_{CO_2} in normal persons. What value we use is within limits arbitrary. There seems to be no good reason for discarding 38° C.—at least it is a round number.

The second aspect of this problem is that of the febrile patient—should one attempt to measure blood pH at the patient's body temperature? When making determinations for clinical purposes I believe not, for the error involved in making measurements at 38° C. when the patient's " body temperature " is 40° C. is not great. For instance, if measurements are made on a blood sample at 40° C. and then repeated at 38° C. the two sets of figures will be roughly as below:

	40° C.	38° C.
pH	7·413	7·442
P_{CO_2} mm. Hg . .	40	37
HCO_3^- mEq./l. . .	25·0	25·1

It may be argued that a blood pH of 7·442 is rather far from the " true " value of 7·413, but the refutation lies in asking what is the normal value for blood pH at 40° C.

(ii) pH Measurement

It is not necessary to spend long on this aspect, which has been and will be discussed by other speakers. There are a few points worth raising however.

(a) **pH Scale.** Obviously before a pH measurement becomes significant in relation to pK′ the same buffer standards must have been used for the determination of both. The corollary is that unless every laboratory is to be expected to carry out its own determination of pK′ some pH scale must be established. I think the Hitchcock-Taylor scale (Hitchcock and Taylor, 1938a and b), or some close approximation, has the best claim for acceptance, firstly on its own merits, and secondly because the most recent and acceptable value for pK′ (Severinghaus *et al.*, 1956b) is on that scale.

(b) **Apparatus.** The type of glass electrode pH apparatus used to measure blood or plasma pH is probably not important, though it is possible that the different liquid junctions in use may produce significant differences in the apparent values. So far as I know there is no study demonstrating this point.

(c) **Blood versus Plasma pH.** It is customary, when using the Henderson-Hasselbalch equation to calculate P_{CO_2}, to determine the pH of whole blood and to assume that this represents the pH of " true " plasma. Until very recently the only evidence that this is in fact so was that of Parsons (1917), who using a hydrogen electrode concluded that the whole blood and plasma pH are identical. Dr. Mattock has mentioned the possibility of the " suspended particle " effect on blood pH (Jenny *et al.*, 1950). Severinghaus *et al.* (1956a) in a very elegant and careful experiment found the pH difference between blood and plasma when separated at 37·5° C., and corrections were applied to allow for glycolysis, to be minimal though not insignificant—blood pH being 0·008 ± 0·007 units lower than that of plasma. If we accept this it implies we should determine both pH and T_{CO_2} on plasma. It leads on however to what is perhaps a more serious and controversial problem.

(d) **True versus Separated Plasma.** pK′ determinations are made using a plasma system. In using pK′ however we generally measure the pH of whole blood (" true " plasma) but determine the total CO_2 on plasma separated from red cells by centrifuging anaerobically at room temperature. Do we in fact have evidence that the constitution of the plasma does not change during the process of separation and re-warming? If there is a change we are using the constant pK′ derived from one system to apply to another.

The first point is that when estimating pH, T_{CO_2} etc., if any degree of accuracy is to be obtained we should, I think, discontinue the practice of collection and centrifugation of the blood sample under paraffin, and collect, transport, store and centrifuge the sample in the same syringe. It is not difficult to arrange, even in routine laboratory practice, and there are then no longer doubts about results on grounds of contact with air.

The real problem, this precaution having been taken, is as to whether this plasma separated at room temperature is " true " plasma. The evidence either for or against is slight. Severinghaus et al. (1956b) found no difference in the total CO_2 of plasma separated at 37° C. or 5° C. This was a careful experiment designed to solve just this problem. On the other hand we have the fragmentary observations of Rosenthal (1948) who found a loss of both chloride and total CO_2 from the plasma during centrifuging at room temperature. Astrup (1956) using blood of high sedimentation rate, though apparently without correction for glycolysis, found that the lower the temperature of separation, the higher the plasma pH, the lower the T_{CO_2} and, using his figures, the lower the P_{CO_2} and HCO_3^-. Thus we have on this most important point two sets of observations with totally opposed results.

It would surprise me very much if there were no change in the ionic constitution and pH of plasma after separation at room temperature and rewarming. This conclusion is based on the very simple observation of Rosenthal (1948) that if a blood or plasma sample is cooled anaerobically, $\delta.\text{pH}/\delta.T°C$ is for whole blood $-0\cdot0147$ and for plasma $-0\cdot0118$. This implies that the temperature coefficient for the pH of the red cell in a closed system is considerably greater than that for plasma.

The principal buffer systems of the red cell are hæmoglobinate and bicarbonate, and of the plasma, proteinate and bicarbonate.

<table>
<tr><td align="center">*Red cell*</td><td align="center">*Plasma*</td></tr>
<tr><td>$\text{pH}=\text{pK}'_{HbO_2}+\log \dfrac{[HbO_2^-]}{[HHbO_2]}$</td><td>$\text{pH}=\text{pK}'_{Pr}+\log \dfrac{[Pr^-]}{[HPr]}$</td></tr>
<tr><td>$\quad=\text{pK}'\quad+\log \dfrac{[HCO_3^-]}{[H_2CO_3]}$</td><td>$\quad=\text{pK}'\quad+\log \dfrac{[HCO_3^-]}{[H_2CO_3]}$</td></tr>
</table>

Likewise the red cell and plasma base can approximately be represented thus:

Red cell

$\Sigma\,BA=BCl+[BHCO_3+BHbO_2]$

Plasma

$\Sigma\,BA=BCl+[BHCO_3+BPr]$

BCl representing " fixed " base, and the bracketed portions " buffer " base.

Now the principal effect of cooling on the acid-base equilibrium of red cell and plasma is on the base binding capacity of HbO_2 or plasma protein. In each case it is reduced, but to a greater degree within the red cell than in plasma.

pK' is identical for the bicarbonate system in red cell and plasma (Dill *et al.*, 1937) and presumably so is the temperature coefficient. The CO_2 tension is also presumably identical in the red cell and plasma. Therefore if we accept Rosenthal's observations as indicating that on cooling there is a greater rise of pH within the red cell than in plasma, one would expect during cooling of blood a shift of bicarbonate, or more probably CO_2, from plasma into red cell, and an increase in [HCO_3^-] therein, with a corresponding shift of Cl^- from red cell to plasma to restore the Donnan equilibrium. If now the plasma is separated from the red cell mass and rewarmed to " body " temperature one would expect just the effects observed by Astrup (1956)—a fall of T_{CO_2} and HCO_3^-, a fall of P_{CO_2} and a rise of pH.

I would suggest therefore that despite the most convincing experiment of Severinghaus *et al.* (1956b) this problem is not solved, and that it needs urgent attention to demonstrate once for all whether " true " and " derived " plasma are identical, and to decide what we should do about it if they are not.

(iii) CO_2 Solubility Factor

Bohr and Bock (1891) originally assumed CO_2 in plasma to behave in a similar fashion to O_2, i.e. its solubility to be 97·5 per cent of that in water. The figures generally accepted now are those of Van Slyke *et al.* (1928) which were directly determined, i.e. at 38° C. 0·0301 m.moles/mm. Hg/l. (or more properly 0·0328 m.moles/mm. Hg/Kg H_2O), for protein appeared to act as an inert substance. There are certain factors which affect this coefficient.

(a) **Ionic Strength.** Added salts have been observed to depress the solubility of CO_2 in plasma (Van Slyke *et al.*, 1928), and from the figures of Hastings and Sendroy (1925) the solubility of CO_2 in an aqueous solution would appear to vary inversely with the ionic strength. Calculations based on their figures suggest that if the solubility in normal plasma of ionic strength, say, 0·015 is 0·0301 m.moles/mm. Hg/l., in plasma of ionic strength 0·105, which is somewhere in the region of the lower limit consistent with life, the solubility factor would be 0·0304—a change producing an insignificant error on calculated P_{CO_2}.

(b) **Plasma Fat.** Of more practical significance may be the observation that in a fatty plasma the solubility factor may be as high as 0·0319 (Van Slyke *et al.*, 1928). This would however give an error in total plasma CO_2 and calculated P_{CO_2} of only about 1 per cent.

(iv) pK'

The most common argument put forward against the validity of the use of the Henderson-Hasselbalch equation to determine P_{CO_2} is that of the possibility of variations of pK' in pathological as opposed to normal plasmas.

(a) **Variation in Normal Plasma.** We must first find an acceptable value for pK' in the plasma of normal persons. As pointed out before, this depends on the buffer system used. The only determination which has significance for the Hitchcock-Taylor scale—and also the most recent—is that of Severinghaus *et al.* (1956b). These workers obtained a value of 6·086 at 37·5° C., or applying a temperature correction, 6·084 at 38° C. The fact that this value agrees well with that of Robinson *et al.* (1934)—viz. 6·092 at 38° C.—is, I suspect, accidental, for the latter workers used a hydrogen electrode and Sørensen's pH scale.

The important point is that, using their value for pK', Severinghaus *et al.* (1956) compared computed and known P_{CO_2} for 20 samples of plasma from 18 normal men and found a mean error of 0·0 mm. Hg with S.D. 0·3, i.e. less than 1 per cent. Similarly the extremes of the values for pK' for normal plasmas which Robinson *et al.* (1934) obtained would give an error in calculating P_{CO_2} of only 2 per cent.

(b) **Variations in Pathological Plasma.** There are some factors which are known to affect pK'.

pH. Severinghaus *et al.* (1956b) found a definite relation of pK' to pH, viz. at 37·5° C., pK' = 6·086 + 0·044 (7·4 − pH). Dill *et al.* (1937) had noticed a similar tendency, though they had not been able to quantitate it, while other workers (Cullen *et al.*, 1925; Robinson *et al.*, 1934) had not observed this effect. It may in fact, as Dr. Mattock suggests, be a glass electrode effect.

Ionic Strength. Hastings and Sendroy (1925) investigated the change in pK' with ionic strength for bicarbonate solutions and found an empirical relation at 38° C.

$$pK' = 6·33 - 0·5\sqrt{I}$$

over a range of ionic strengths of 0·01 to 0·18. This has never been confirmed for plasma, though it seems likely that a similar relation would be found. However, calculations based on these figures show that an ionic strength of 0·105 in plasma would alter pK′ to give an error in calculated P_{CO_2} of about 2·5 per cent.

Temperature. pK′ varies markedly with temperature (Severinghaus *et al.*, 1956b), but this should not concern us for there is little reason to determine pH at a temperature other than that at which pK′ was measured.

Variation with other Factors. There is lacking a modern study of pK′ in plasma from patients suffering from gross disorders of the plasma constituents. Robinson *et al.* (1934) determined pK′ in 12 normal plasmas and in 53 plasmas from patients suffering from a variety of diseases. They could find no significant difference in the values obtained for the two groups. The limits of pK′ at 38° C. were 6·071–6·117, the maximum deviation from the mean being sufficient to give a 5 per cent. error in calculated P_{CO_2}.

(v) Total Plasma CO₂

The sources of error involved in determining this factor by the manometric method of Van Slyke (Peters and Van Slyke, 1932) are often neglected, particularly in routine laboratories. There are two major sources of error which are worth discussing.

(a) **Calibration Errors.** In this country at least the calibration of the chamber is frequently in error. This is in some cases due to the fact that mercury has been used for calibration without allowance for the difference between a water and mercury meniscus. By performing a recalibration with water as originally described, errors of up to 3 per cent have been observed, which can of course be corrected for. A confirmatory overall check may be made using standard solutions of sodium carbonate. On the same subject, the pipettes used for the delivery of the plasma sample should also be checked for accuracy of calibration.

(b) **Anæsthetic Gases.** A very great potential source of error is the presence of anæsthetic gases or volatile liquids in the plasma sample. Error from this can be partly, if not completely, corrected by the use of a modification in the method, such as that of Goldstein *et al.* (1950).

Conclusions

There exists at the present time an impression that the values for P_{CO_2} in plasma obtained by calculations from the Henderson-Hasselbalch equation are not of great accuracy. Yet analysis of the possible errors shows that individually they are not of great magnitude. When more than one is involved there may in fact be significant errors, though this has not been demonstrated.

In other words it would appear that the answers to the questions posed at the beginning are that the method is quite acceptable for clinical purposes and probably satisfies the criteria for most research projects, provided the sources of error are recognized, and either corrected or avoided.

REFERENCES

ASTRUP, P. (1956). A Simple Electrometric Technique for the Determination of Carbon Dioxide Tension in Blood and Plasma, Total Content of Carbon Dioxide in Plasma, and Bicarbonate Content in "Separated" Plasma at a Fixed Carbon Dioxide Tension (40 mm. Hg). *Scand. J. clin. Lab. Invest.*, **8**, 33.

BOHR, C., BOCK, J. (1891). Bestimmung der Absorption einiger Gase in Wasser bei den Temperaturen zwischen 0 und 100°. *Wied. Ann. Physik. u. Chem.*, **44**, 318.

BUYTENDYK, F. J. J., BRINKMAN, R., and MOOK, H. W. (1927). Determination of the True Dissociation-Constant of Carbonic Acid. *Biochem. J.*, **21**, 576.

CULLEN, G. E., KEELER, H. R., and ROBINSON, H. W. (1925). The pK' of the Henderson-Hasselbalch Equation for Hydrion Concentration of Serum. *J. biol. Chem.*, **66**, 301.

DILL, D. B., DALY, C., and FORBES, W. H. (1937). The pK' of Serum and Red Cells. *J. biol. Chem.*, **117**, 569.

GOLDSTEIN, F., GIBBON, J. H., ALLBRITTEN, F. F., and STAYMAN, J. W. (1950). The Combined Manometric Determination of Oxygen and Carbon Dioxide in Blood in the Presence of Low Concentrations of Ethyl Ether. *J. biol. Chem.* **182**, 815.

HASSELBALCH, K. A. (1916). Die Berechnung der Wasserstoffzahl des Blutes aus der freien und gebundenen Kohlensäure desselben, und die Sauerstoffbindung des Blutes als Funktion der Wasserstoffzahl. *Biochem. Z.*, **78**, 112.

HASTINGS, A. B., and SENDROY, J. (1925). The Effect of Variation in Ionic Strength on the Apparent First and Second Dissociation Constants of Carbonic Acid. *J. biol. Chem.*, **65**, 445.

HENDERSON, L. J. (1908). Concerning the Relationship between the Strength of Acids and their Capacity to Preserve Neutrality. *Amer. J. Physiol.*, **21**, 173.

HENDERSON, L. J. (1908). The Theory of Neutrality Regulation in the Animal Organism. *Amer. J. Physiol.*, **21**, 427.

HITCHCOCK, D. I., and TAYLOR, A. C. (1937). The Standardization of Hydrogen Ion Determinations. I. Hydrogen Electrode Measurements with a Liquid Junction. *J. Amer. chem. Soc.*, **59**, 1812.

HITCHCOCK, D. I., and TAYLOR, A. C. (1938). The Standardization of Hydrogen Ion Determinations. II. A Standardization of the pH Scale at 38° C. *J. Amer. chem. Soc.*, **60**, 2710.

JENNY, H., NIELSON, T. R., COLEMAN, N. T., and WILLIAMS, D. E. (1950). Concerning the Measurement of pH, Ion Activities, and Membrane Potentials in Colloidal Systems. *Science*, **112**, 164.

PARSONS, T. R. (1917). On the Reaction of the Blood in the Body. *J. Physiol.*, **51**, 440.

PETERS, J. P., and VAN SLYKE, D. D. (1932). *Quantitative Clinical Chemistry: Methods.* Baillière, Tindall and Cox, London.

ROBINSON, H. W., PRICE, J. W., and CULLEN, G. E. (1934). The Value of pK′ in the Henderson-Hasselbalch Equation for Human and Dog Sera, determined with the Simms Electrode. *J. biol. Chem.*, **106**, 7.

ROSENTHAL, T. B. (1948). The Effect of Temperature on the pH of Blood and Plasma *in vitro*. *J. biol. Chem.*, **173**, 25.

SEVERINGHAUS, J. W., STUPFEL, M., and BRADLEY, A. F. (1956). Accuracy of Blood pH and P_{CO_2} Determinations. *J. appl. Physiol.*, **9**, 189.

SEVERINGHAUS, J. W., STUPFEL, M., and BRADLEY, A. F. (1956). Variations of Serum Carbonic Acid pK′ with pH and Temperature. *J. appl. Physiol.*, **9**, 197.

VAN SLYKE, D. D., SENDROY, J., HASTINGS, B., and NEILL, J. M. (1928). Studies of Gas and Electrolyte Equilibria in Blood. *J. biol. Chem.*, **78**, 765.

DISCUSSION

Chairman: I will ask Professor Neil to open this discussion.

Neil: First and foremost about the Henderson-Hasselbalch equation: Homer Smith once described it as " a monument to human laziness " and I thoroughly agree with him. I think it is mostly a waste of time, because it is a second order usage. You determine things and put them in an equation. You use factors, and in certain cases, of course, the people who are using those factors have determined them themselves and correspondingly know exactly what they are doing. Other people—and you remember if you advertise the use of the Henderson-Hasselbalch equation, there *will* be other people—make use of these factors without understanding that they are rushing in where angels fear to tread. I like to deal with blood as blood, equilibrated to the tension that I know in the tonometer, and measure the pH at the temperature of equilibration; and I thought we might perhaps discuss some of the points which Mr. Ludbrook raised by considering, first, blood as blood: secondly, plasma as plasma; and thirdly, hæmoglobin solutions as hæmoglobin solutions, and see how very differently they behave with respect to temperature.

If you take some blood and equilibrate it at 37° C. or 26° C., or 12° C. in this case, with a variety of CO_2 tensions (Fig. 1), you find

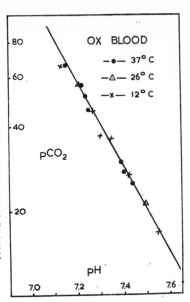

FIG. 1. Log P_{CO_2}/pH line of ox blood. Blood was equilibrated at 37° C. with a series of CO_2 tensions and the pH of the equilibrated samples were read at 37° C. The process was repeated with blood equilibrated at 26° C. and the pH readings were made at 26° C. Finally equilibrations and pH readings were made at 12° C. The points obtained lie virtually on the same log P_{CO_2}/pH line. When equilibrated at P_{CO_2} of 40 mm. at 37° C. the pH measured at 37° C. was 7·31. The same blood sample when allowed to cool to 26° C. gave a pH value measured at 26° C. of 7·47 (this would correspond to a P_{CO_2} of about 22–23 mm. Hg). Lastly when the blood was cooled to 12° C. its pH value was 7·67 at 12° C. which would correspond to a P_{CO_2} of about 12 mm. Hg).

that the log P_{CO_2}/pH line that you get for blood—it does not matter whether it is ox blood or human blood—is much the same. The points lie virtually on the same log P_{CO_2}/pH line. If you take a sample of blood from the patient at 37° and you centrifuge it at, say, a room temperature of 12° C. anaerobically, it follows of course that, having centrifuged it, withdrawing the so-called true plasma, you find the pH measured at 12° C. much higher; then correspondingly the P_{CO_2} must be lower; the P_{CO_2} must have fallen.

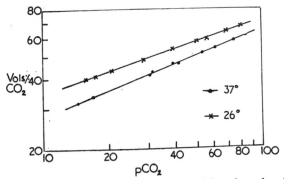

FIG. 2. Human blood dissociation curves (plotted as log lines) determined at 37° C. and at 26° C. respectively. Note that blood equilibrated at 37° C. with a P_{CO_2} of 40 mm. Hg if then allowed to cool anaerobically will necessarily re-equilibrate and show a lower P_{CO_2}—in this case about 23 mm. Hg.

You can see that much more simply if you deal with the CO_2 dissociation curve (Fig. 2), where you merely equilibrate the blood at 37° C. and you equilibrate it at 26° C. Now it was equilibrated, let's say, at 40 mm. Hg; that is its content then. And when you centrifuge it at 26° C., its content must remain the same and correspondingly you come out on this 26° C. line—these are plotted as log lines of course—and therefore the P_{CO_2} must have dropped to about 23 mm. Hg. It is as simple as that. But the blood CO_2 content is the same, therefore the tension must be less.

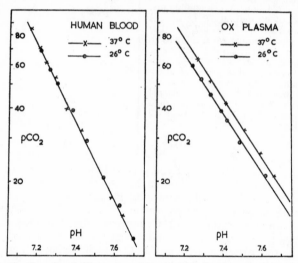

FIG. 3. Log P_{CO_2}/pH graphs of human blood and of separated ox plasma both equilibrated at 37° C. and at 26° C. respectively. Note that the log P_{CO_2}/pH line of separated plasma equilibrated at 26° C. lies to the left of that equilibrated at 37° C., unlike the behaviour seen with blood itself.

Now, it is an odd thing about blood keeping the same pH/P_{CO_2} line at different temperatures of equilibration because plasma behaves quite differently (Fig. 3). Ox plasma, there's the line at 37° C. P_{CO_2} against pH; here is the line at 26° C. In other words, at 26° C. the pH at a given tension of CO_2 will be more acid, so to speak—it will have a higher hydrogen ion content—than at 37° C. Correspondingly, if you were to cool plasma which had been equilibrated at 37° C. down to 26° C. then the new tension of equilibration would be about 25 mm. Hg. The pH then would be about 7·55. Well that of course could be predicted roughly from the use of the Henderson-Hasselbalch equation. In other words, if you took a plasma containing 25 milliequivalents of bicarbonate and 1·25 milliequivalents of H_2CO_3 expressed as CO_2 at 37° C., that is a total of 26·25 mEq./l., if you cool it down to 26° C. the tension is about 25 mm. Hg by the time you have finished cooling; the solubility factor is ·0411, so you have roughly 1 milliequivalent of CO_2 present as carbonic acid. That drop in carbonic acid content, 1·25 to 1, is being made up by the increase in bicarbonate content, which is at the expense of the diminished ionization of the plasma proteins. Plasma then behaves that way. Instead of " staying on the same line," so to speak, it goes acid. As blood stays on the same P_{CO_2}/pH line, obviously hæmoglobin must go the other way.

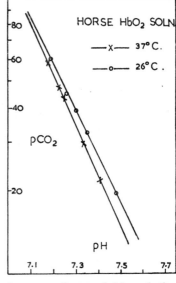

FIG. 4. Log P_{CO_2}/pH lines of a hæmo-globin solution equilibrated at 37° C. and 26° C. respectively. Note that the log P_{CO_2}/pH line at 26° C. lies to the right of that at 37° C.

Fig. 4 shows that it does. This is a pure hæmoglobin solution and that really is my excuse for talking to you because, as far as I know, except for the data we published at the International Congress of Physiology in 1956 there are no data on hæmoglobin ionization at different temperatures. A hæmoglobin solution becomes more alkaline at a given tension when you lower the temperature of equilibration, the reason being, of course, the diminished ionization of the hæmoglobin which is itself an acid. You have, then, when you cool blood, during centrifugation, a rather complex system. The hæmoglobin which is going one way and the plasma, the tendency of which is to go the other and the end result is the same. I should think myself that it would be very certain that there would be redistribution of bicarbonate in much the same way as Astrup said. I should be most surprised if the CO_2 content remained the same, but as I indicated by that simple calculation, it *could* be quite similar, and yet the pH is altered very much.

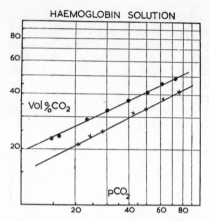

FIG. 5. Dissociation curves of hæmoglobin solution (plotted as log lines) determined at 37° C. (crosses) and 26° C. (circles) respectively. The CO_2 carrying power of the solution is greater at the lower temperature.

Fig. 5 shows another variation on the theme; with the hæmo-globin solution at 26° C. (the upper one) you could expect the carrying power for CO_2 to be higher than at 37° C.; the reason simply being the diminished ionization of the hæmoglobin at that lower temperature.

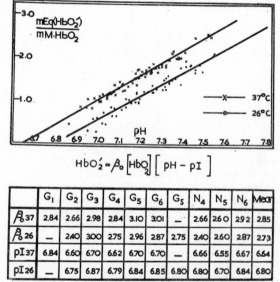

$$HbO_2' = \beta_o \left[HbO_2\right] \left[pH - pI\right]$$

	G_1	G_2	G_3	G_4	G_5	G_6	G_S	N_4	N_5	N_6	Mean
$\beta_o 37$	2.84	2.66	2.98	2.84	3.10	3.01	—	2.66	2.60	2.92	2.85
$\beta_o 26$	—	2.40	3.00	2.75	2.96	2.87	2.75	2.40	2.60	2.87	2.73
$pI 37$	6.84	6.60	6.70	6.62	6.70	6.70	—	6.66	6.55	6.67	6.64
$pI 26$	—	6.75	6.87	6.79	6.84	6.85	6.80	6.80	6.70	6.84	6.80

FIG. 6. The ionization of horse hæmoglobin. Collected results from ten different preparations. In the graph: ordinate = $mEq[HbO_2^-]$ per mM. HbO_2; abscissa = pH values. The points are determined experimentally. The lines are calculated from the buffer equation using the constants in the table. The table shows the $\beta_{o_{37}}$, $\beta_{o_{26}}$, pI_{37} and pI_{26} of the ten solutions and their means.

Here is actually the result of estimations of 10 pure solutions of horse hæmoglobin. Pure crystals were made. They were dissolved in a suitable medium to give something like blood in ionic concentration and in CO_2 carrying power; one then proceeded along the well-worn lines indicated by Van Slyke and his colleagues and worked out the buffer equation for hæmoglobin ionization (Fig. 6).

$$[HbO_2^-] = \beta_0 \, [HbO_2] \, (pH - pI)$$

where $[HbO_2^-]$ is the concentration of oxyhæmoglobin anions, β_0 is a factor (2·85 at 37° C. and 2·73 at 26° C.), $[HbO_2]$ is the millimolar concentration of HbO_2, pI is a constant, similar to, but not necessarily identical with, the isoelectric point. The respective values of pI at 37° C. and at 26° C. are 6·64 and 6·80.

If $[HbO_2]$ is 9 millimoles per litre the solution would contain $9 \times 1·67$ g. HbO_2 (i.e. 15 g./100 ml.).

The figure shows that the ionization of oxyhæmoglobin at any given pH is less at 26° C. than it would be at 37° C.

Now where the difficulties arise, in considering all these buffer systems and their contribution, is that blood is a heterogenous system. In the corpuscle hæmoglobin is not at the pH of plasma, and until one has studied the behaviour of oxyhæmoglobin in such solutions of ionic strength and pH as exists in a corpuscle, one will not be able to slip facilely from the application of the above equation, derived in these solutions, to blood itself.

Ramwell: I would like to make a number of points about Mr. Ludbrook's paper. I was surprised that for clinical work he went to the trouble of spinning blood instead of just Van Slyking whole blood and using the Singer Hastings nomogram. The other point is that I have been doing some work with the artificial kidney and I have measured the pK's of the blood of some of these patients, and though I found the standard error of the mean a little greater in these extremely acidotic individuals, I too could not find a significant difference between the two pK's, and therefore on a new subject I continue to use the Singer Hastings nomogram. The other point was about calibration of the Van Slyke chamber. I have calibrated quite a few—and maybe it is the people I buy them off—but I have not found them more than ·01 out at the 2 ml. mark and that helps of course. As for volatile gases, I think it all depends on the anæsthetist you are working with. If you can persuade him to work with oxygen instead of nitrous oxide or ether, so much the better.

Astrup: We now use the Conway method for the determination of total CO_2 and I can recommend it. It is, in our hands, more accurate than the Van Slyke method.

Severinghaus: I would like to ask Dr. Astrup in view of this discussion whether the temperature of centrifugation of blood makes a difference in the CO_2 content. I have never been able to see the actual data themselves. How much difference does it make? We have centrifuged triplicate samples at 0°, 25° and 37° C. and found no difference greater than 0·1 m.moles.

Astrup: It was not over 1 m.mole, between 26·5 and 27, between 25·5 and 26·5. But we ought to have repeated these experiments.

Severinghaus: Was this just one sample or is this the mean of a lot?

Astrup: It was the mean of two or three samples as far as I remember.

Nunn: The question of the partition of CO_2 between plasma and cells at different temperatures is of great importance in correcting for the difference in P_{CO_2} of blood at different temperatures. Bradley, Stupfel and Severinghaus (1956) have given an excellent method of correcting the measured blood P_{CO_2} for the patient's body temperature; but this all rests on the assumption that the CO_2 content of plasma is independent of temperature. There is, however, a considerable quantity of evidence to show that this assumption is true. Joffe and Poulton, in 1920, found it so, as did Severinghaus, Stupfel and Bradley (1956). I have also analysed the data of Brewin, Gould, Nashat and Neil (1955). Their results are compatible with the partition of CO_2 between plasma and cells remaining constant at 26° and 37° C.

Neil: Yes, well I am not disputing that the CO_2 *content* may remain about the same in the plasma. I mean, Severinghaus shows that. I am not disputing that at all. What I am pointing out is the very important difference in how the CO_2 is distributed in the plasma. In other words, some of it is now as CO_2, some of it is as bicarbonate. I would be interested, in other words, to hear an explanation of how—as the Donnan equilibrium is dependent on the concentration of protein ions in the cell—how it is that, with a fall of temperature which reduces that ionic concentration, you could not have a redistribution of bicarbonate. I mean, you cannot get round that. And as I say, if you take blood and equilibrate it at 37° and then cool it down to 26° anaerobically, as the content is the same, the P_{CO_2} must have fallen to 20-odd mm. Hg; it will depend on what sort of blood it is and how much hæmoglobin it contains. The dispute is *not* that it may be about the same, or just the same, or should not be; it is surely that there has been an entirely different distribution of the two components which is responsible, of course, for the considerable change in the pH.

Nunn: Then we must regard it as just a fortunate coincidence that the plasma CO_2 content should remain constant.

Neil: It is as fortunate as the coincidence of the 37/26 line and it is bound up with that sort of thing.

Chairman: I am not sure that it is quite right to call this coincidence fortunate. To me indeed it would be unfortunate if it succeeded in hiding an error of which, but for the coincidence, we might have become aware earlier.

REFERENCES

BRADLEY, A. F., STUPFEL, M., and SEVERINGHAUS, J. W. (1956). Effect of Temperature on P_{CO_2} and P_{O_2} of Blood in Vitro. *J. Appl. Physiol.*, **9**, 201.

BREWIN, E. G., GOULD, R. P., NASHAT, F. S., and NEIL, E. (1955). An Investigation of Problems of Acid-base Equilibrium in Hypothermia. *Guys Hosp. Rep.*, **104**, 177.

JOFFE, J., and POULTON, E. P. (1920). The Partition of CO_2 Between Plasma and Corpuscles in Oxygenated and Reduced Blood. *J. Physiol.*, **54**, 129.

SEVERINGHAUS, J. W., STUPFEL, M., and BRADLEY, A. F. (1956). Accuracy of Blood pH and P_{CO_2} Determinations. *J. Appl. Physiol.*, **9**, 189.

VI. FIRST GENERAL DISCUSSION

Chairman: The time has now come for the discussion to be general and not directed to one particular paper. One of the things which struck me was the interest aroused generally by the concept that we should try and get a better degree of standardization, for instance with our buffers and with our methods, and perhaps we might start off by directing the conversation towards that idea.

Ludbrook: We are suggesting a pH scale on this occasion when we are specifically concerned with biological pH measurement. Is there any reason why we should have one primary standard buffer? Would it not be better to have two—roughly pH 4 and 9 or 6·84 and 9? Those using this scale will for the most part be using glass electrode systems which they will want to calibrate themselves by means of at least two buffers to determine the millivolt-pH ratio of the electrode. It would seem to me then perhaps simpler and more practical to have two " primary " standards straddling the biological pH range.

Mattock: Quite apart from the purely etymological aspect, surely one cannot have two primary standards. If you have standardized with buffer 6·835, your borax, although it may be 9·20, or something like that, may in fact for various reasons read 9·15. Now if you start from the other end standardizing with your 9·20, then your phosphate is going to be 6·88, or thereabouts. Now you may make a correction or you may not and it seems to me—I am not absolutely clear about this because it has just been thrown at me and I have not thought about it—there is a catch in it.

Wynn: It raises the question that Dr. Severinghaus mentioned. Is it, in fact, difficult to make up these phosphate buffers at 6·835, 6·836, whichever you accept? We have not found them particularly difficult to make up. Have you had practical experience of difficulty in making them up and getting reproducible figures?

Severinghaus: No. The reports of others mention it. I think we would all agree though that we do need two accepted standards so that we can calibrate our electrodes. Beyond that it is only a matter of words which one calls primary. If you agree that both the two solutions have a pH value which you know, then you make your machine read correctly on both of them.

Lauchlan: In the original Committee meetings on the pH scales held by the British Standards this question of phosphate or phthalate arose and the chemical manufacturers did throw considerable cold water on the idea of producing a primary standard on a phosphate owing to the difficulty of getting the necessary purity and the uncertainties of hydration. I think it was felt that the Bureau of

Standards' suggestion of phthalate was a better one. It can be produced in a high state of purity with, really, considerable ease.

Mattock: I must say that in conversation with one or two manufacturers of chemicals that they were particularly unhappy about the choice of phthalate. We have found difficulties in work with a hydrogen electrode which is not quite the same in this context. Certainly one can have difficulty in measuring the pH of phthalate solution, or measuring millivolts from a phthalate solution with a hydrogen electrode, whether it be palladium or platinum, because of poisoning which does not occur with other solutions. The phthalate buffer in itself has not got particularly good characteristics in so far as buffer capacity is concerned, and it is removed from the blood pH range with which we are concerned. It means that you have to start calibrating a long way away; it means that your meter has to be calibrated so that you can utilize it for reading, which means that you have then to shift your scale quite a lot, which means you have then to apply millivolts in some way or the scale has to be correspondingly inaccurate because it will have to accommodate a large pH range. If you apply millivolts you are liable to get errors. The problem is then one of instrument manufacture, and also various other aspects of the fact that your pH is a long way removed from your measured pH. I must say one should recrystallize one's phosphates, but we have never actually observed trouble ourselves.

Lauchlan: If the preparation of the phosphate is as uncertain as the error of the pH meter, we might as well make use of the primary standard which we have already.

Mattock: Well, I don't think it is, frankly.

Lauchlan: It may be improved in manufacture.

Severinghaus: In each case do you recrystallize your phosphate?

Mattock: We do recrystallize usually.

Severinghaus: And you would recommend that as a primary standard?

Mattock: Yes. But I do not think that recrystallization would necessarily be required. I am quite sure Mr. Ludbrook has not recrystallized, and I do not think you have, have you, Dr. Nunn?

Chairman: I will put that to the meeting in general. Have those of us who have been using these buffers been in the habit of recrystallizing their phosphates? Or not? I take it not.

Nunn: My practice is to calibrate our glass electrode each morning between the phthalate and the borate, and then to compare blood with phosphate. I think that is what most of us do. In which case surely we are using the phosphate as a primary buffer.

Severinghaus: Well then you have three, and you like them all three to read correctly?

Nunn: Yes.

Severinghaus: And they do in fact?

Nunn: Pretty nearly.

Campbell: What you want, then, is that the scale between two extremes shall be known within reasonable confidence limits, and if you then compare the blood with something which is close to blood the errors introduced by liquid junction and its variations are going to be small. I think that we should, with the available data, decide which is the worse error, the error in preparing the chemical solution, or the error introduced by being a long way away. It seems that phthalate has got things in its favour in terms of our being able to prepare it in a certain concentration and purity, but it is a long way away from blood. 6·835 is easy to prepare and better known than things in the 7·3–7·4 range, but it is further away from blood. Now, we should be able to beat this out with the talent available. Could we have a ruling, Sir, from the group on how much error one may introduce in using a buffer of 6·835 allowing for troubles with phosphate preparation. How much error are we likely to introduce?

Mattock: There are some data on liquid junction errors which Bates obtained. He standardized his system with the phosphate buffer and then measured the pH of phthalate and borate with solutions involving a liquid junction and he found something like 0·001 to 0·002 error with the phthalate and with borate he found 0·003, going in opposite directions. In other words, the errors were additive, so that your error on one side of the phosphate was one way, and the other way on the other side. So if you standardize the phthalate and then go to a blood pH somewhat higher than the phosphate you may get an error of the order—this is purely on liquid junction grounds—of the order of 0·003. I would not like to commit myself on other factors because it is very difficult to pin down the figures. One reason for suggesting phosphate is to try to eliminate those errors. I must confess that this problem of preparing phosphate had just not occurred to me because we just have not heard of it before.

Campbell: If, in fact, the differences between phthalate and phosphate are as small as that I would have thought they were small compared with the difficulties introduced by reading blood which is a long way away from your buffer. In which case there is a case to be made out for agreeing on using a buffer which is much closer to blood.

Severinghaus: I did not think that anyone was suggesting that one read blood against either the phthalate or borate buffers, but that a buffer in the seven range be standardized against them.

Campbell: No. But do we use a 6·835 or do we also use something that is still closer to the blood? Because if I followed Dr. Wright properly, some of the errors which he found when using blood rather than buffers could introduce quite significant errors —of the order of 0·01, 0·02—if you are as far away as you are from 6·835.

Wright: I have been wondering whether there is any reason for not making up a phosphate buffer in different ratios from the ordinary one to give you virtually any pH you like in this range.

Wynn: There is a reason, and that is its buffer capacity is rather reduced at 7·4 and therefore its stability is, in fact, not great.

Wright: But if one were picking a new buffer?

Mattock: I do not feel that a new primary buffer is to be looked on as practical. The enormous amount of work done at the National Bureau of Standards since 1945 cannot be laughed at and in fact, you know, the phthalate buffer of the British Standard is based on the work of Manov *et al.*, who were working at the National Bureau of Standards.

Campbell: In that case is it the feeling we should not run into these errors in liquid junction potentials, but rather settle for 6·835?

Mattock: Well, that is my feeling.

Chairman: It seems to me that this is one of the fundamental questions we are here to solve. What accuracy do we need? Those of us who are measuring just for clinical purposes would be quite happy with the accuracy we already have. Those of us who are measuring for more strictly scientific purposes must always be urged on in the pursuit of ever greater accuracy—of that extra decimal point. Many of us here are clinicians. We are concerned purely with measuring for clinical purposes. I think we would probably be quite happy as we are, providing we all agree on standards and on methods of presentation. But it may be that some of you have rather different ideas.

Campbell: Dr. Wynn here has said that the phosphate buffers in the range 7·2–7·4 are somewhat unstable. Do you mean by that that they are unstable in the course of time or they are unstable in the hydrogen ion concentration they produce in the measuring instrument?

Wynn: No. Over the course of time.

Campbell: Well, in fact, I think most of us who have used phosphate buffers do in fact prepare them fresh each time from the two primary phosphates—one at each end; and in this case I would not have thought the argument came out very strongly against them.

Wynn: There is a case, however, for not having to do any preparation at all from day to day. Now, I understand you make up your buffers fresh each day, Dr. Severinghaus, isn't that so?

Severinghaus: Well, we use one of these concentrates so we dilute up a fresh batch for each use, perhaps not every day.

Wynn: What is its pH in your laboratory when you measure blood pH?

Severinghaus: We are using one that is listed as 7·00 ± ·01 and is, in fact, 7·06.

Wynn: Well, that is quite acceptable.

Severinghaus: It is more convenient than using phthalate or borate routinely.

Wynn: Yes, quite. But you have to make it up every day. As I remember it, it is not a very difficult task.

Severinghaus: No. It involves dirtying one pipette.

Wynn: Yes. But we do not even have to do that, but you may not think that that is important.

Chairman: I think there is a good deal to be said for establishing a routine in a laboratory by which the workers are, as it were, compelled to make up their buffer every day. It keeps them on their toes, and I would have much more confidence in a laboratory that did that than one that took its buffer off the shelf where it had remained for two or three months.

Campbell: Could I ask Dr. Wynn if he thinks the difficulty of making up a fresh phosphate buffer each day (which is, I agree, the work of dirtying one pipette) is so great that it is not to be compared with the possible error introduced by comparing your blood with a buffer which is much further off.

Wynn: No. I think I would be inclined to agree with Dr. Campbell and to do as he suggests, or as Dr. Severinghaus does.

Pask: If you set up on buffer that is separated by a long distance, are you not then becoming very dependent upon the linearity of your potentiometer; and what sort of linearity can one expect from an electrical instrument and how well will it maintain it? I make this deliberate point, having bought what seemed to me a very expensive helical potentiometer and then recalibrated it against a standard on two or three occasions.

Severinghaus: We have had the same experience. I think that someone who is interested in extreme accuracy must check the linearity of his instrument.

Pask: How well does it stick?

Severinghaus: Versus time? Over the course of two years there was no measurable change in a Cambridge instrument, but there were significant variations from linearity which had to be corrected from a correction table with every pH measurement.

Pask: Of course, this makes the idea of a couple of standards which more or less straddle the range of interest to be very attractive in the sense that it minimizes the importance of alinearity, so to speak.

Severinghaus: No, I would not agree with that. If we had a buffer at 7·0 which we knew exactly and never measured anything at 4 or 9 we would have still made large errors because the alinearity of the instrument is not necessarily spread over the whole scale but it varies over small increments of the range and there are significant errors in a change of 0·1 of pH in the instrument.

Pask: Yes. But surely, electrically speaking, you could spread your whole scale over this narrower pH range and you would surely be minimizing the effect.

Lauchlan: Where it is a wound slide wire, that is a spiral wound on a bobbin, the spacing between two turns might correspond to

0·01 pH. Now if that were carelessly wound you could, at one point, get a quite serious error, but which, taken as a percentage over the full scale, would be small. I think that is the point you really want to remember. And I think your helical potentiometer might be more subject to trouble because of bending the wire in wrapping it round whatever it is wrapped round, than, in say, a straight spiral of wire, or wire on a large former. It is the opening of the turns where you bend it which seems to produce the error.

Hill: I think I would be ready to agree with Dr. Lauchlan. I prefer one wound on a large former rather than a helical type.

Ramwell: I think a lot of the points that have been raised are relatively trivial when it comes to measuring actual blood pH as opposed to measuring buffers. There is an error which has not been mentioned, the error involved in actually getting the blood. Not everybody can take blood samples, they often get bubbles in the syringe, sometimes whilst transporting it. There are errors in icing and in filling the dead space with heparin, and some people use sodium fluoride which apparently may alter the pK too. There seem to be so many errors here that I often feel that some of these fine points that have just been raised by Dr. Mattock are very, very small when one thinks about the total error in the sampling of arterial blood and measurement of the pH.

Chairman: It is often said that " The good is the enemy of the best," and if you have something quite good you rest content and do not attempt to improve it any further. Nevertheless, many of us—all of us here who are investigators—have this constant urge to do better still and nothing you say or I say will stop them. Indeed, I should be the last to discourage them.

Ramwell: Can we deal with this point of Dr. Campbell's?

Campbell: Well, I am not motivated by anything except convenience in this respect, and I find no difficulty in preparing a buffer fresh each day which is close to blood. If the difficulties with the pH/e.m.f. relationship introduce an error if you use a buffer a long way away then that is why we should use a buffer which is close to the blood as against one which agrees with some international scale or other. I have been trying to get the meeting to tell me which is the greater error. At the moment I am coming to the conclusion that one is better off using a buffer close to the blood, than using a much better known buffer a long way away and letting other errors creep in.

Severinghaus: I think that we ought to answer that you can have your cake and eat it too because you can use a buffer which is close to blood and check its pH against an internationally agreed standard.

Campbell: Well, yes, that is what we do. People have, however, used the term " straddle " for blood pH's using buffers from 6·8 up to 9. That is a pretty big stride, I should have thought.

Mattock: Yes, but you see, Dr. Severinghaus is right, actually.

What he says is quite consistent, because if you standardize the system in terms of 6·835 and use another buffer subsequently, you are still doing it with reference to a well-known buffer and that is the important thing.

Campbell: So we have our cake and eat it.

Wynn: You have not had your cake and eaten it because the original errors inherent in your glass electrode system are still there in measuring, whether you make up a buffer at say 7·4 or blood at 7·4, so you may as well not have that buffer at 7·4, quite frankly.

Nunn: There is a further source of error in that you are making two comparisons: blood with a 7·4 buffer and then the 7·4 buffer with the 6·835 buffer.

Astrup: In Copenhagen we used a phosphate buffer which has a pH of 7·360 and of course we ran into trouble with the set pH value of this buffer. We solved the problem by taking the pK value of plasma to be 6·11 because it is the commonest value found in the literature. At least it is close to the value found by Van Slyke, and from this value 6·11 we fixed the pH of our buffer to 7·36 by determining total CO_2 and pH in about 25 samples of plasma after equilibration at a known P_{CO_2} (about 40 mm. Hg.), then inserting the values in the Henderson-Hasselbalch equation. Later on the pH value was determined by a hydrogen electrode and was found to be nearly the same. We are now repeating our experiments for determining the pK value for a lot of samples of plasma, but I think what we must do is to compare our phosphate buffer with the buffers of the National Bureau of Standards so that we can get the same values.

Lauchlan: As a manufacturer of instruments I feel it would be nice if we could get some ruling on the accuracies required. Am I correct in assuming, from the conversation, that there are really two standards, a clinical and a research standard? The clinical perhaps being rather lower. Is that heretical?

Brooks: I think that is almost true. I think what Dr. Campbell is really looking for is a buffer and a pH system with which he can come back from holiday, take it off the shelf in a darkened lab. and test a pH of blood accurately enough for clinical purposes, and also to use for research purposes if he so desires.

Severinghaus: Well it would be unfortunate, I think, if you, as a manufacturer, left the meeting with the idea that you should supply poor grade instruments to clinicians. And for another reason I think we ought to ask for instruments which are capable of discriminating down to ·001, so that you can at least see that difference. This is not the accuracy, but then at least the instrument itself will not limit us in our ability to make measurements.

Brooks: I agree. One should be able to measure pH to an accuracy demanded by the situation.

Campbell: I must just protest if it has been felt that I suggested there were any particular conditions in which I think the pH meter should be used. There are several errors here and Dr. Severinghaus said I could have my cake and eat it and Dr. Wynn said I could not. I am trying to find out which I could do: have it or eat it?

Wynn: Dr. Severinghaus raises a very important point. There is really very little difference between the accuracy required in clinical work and research work. In any case, it is not entirely accuracy we want, it is reproducibility, reliability, speed and convenience. Those are all equally desirable, I think. There is not time set aside in this Symposium for the discussion of some of the characteristics of blood pH instruments and so I should like to spend 30 seconds mentioning one or two points about this. In my opinion, for clinical work it is important to have a mains-operated instrument, and I say this because with a battery-operated instrument, however well maintained, there are problems which can occur in the early hours of the morning which may have unfortunate clinical results. You cannot deal with a flat battery at that inconvenient time and you cannot afford to wait around for the results. For this reason I believe that it is necessary in clinical work to have a pH machine which is left switched on day and night. This eliminates completely the warming up period. It is also desirable that if the machine is left on it can be safely left for months at a time. It is for this reason that I much prefer a mains-operated instrument. This is especially the case if they can be combined with the necessary degree of accuracy and convenience of operation, such as is available in modern instruments.

Hill: Well, in our case, in the College we do not usually encounter emergencies, at least not the kind Dr. Wynn has encountered, and we do have battery-operated equipment because of its stability and we do not have any trouble at all. I can of course see his point, in the circumstances, of needing mains-operated equipment. I did want to ask one question: Dr. Wright in his paper was talking about measuring potential differences of the order of 20 microvolts, which strikes me as being a very accurate measurement. Could I ask him to state very briefly how in fact he did measure to this high degree of precision?

Wright: The standard deviation of successive readings of the meter I was using was a matter of $\pm$ 25 microvolts. You can read a figure on the dial of 10 microvolts, but it is not a significant one.

Hill: And this had a built-in standard to check with, did it?

Wright: Yes. Another small point about battery-operated machines: with this one of mine, I use large car type accumulators and they need charging only every three months.

Severinghaus: Another point about this is, it is not uniformly to be expected that a mains-operated instrument warms up faster than a battery-operated one: on the contrary.

Wynn: Ours is left on permanently.

Second Session

VII. THE ACCURACY OF THE MEASUREMENT OF BLOOD P_{CO_2} BY THE INTERPOLATION TECHNIQUE

J. F. Nunn, Ph.D., M.B., F.F.A.R.C.S.

Leverhulme Research Fellow
Research Department of Anæsthetics, Royal College of Surgeons

DETERMINATION of the arterial P_{CO_2} during anæsthesia may be complicated by the presence of anæsthetic gases in the blood. Nitrous oxide, in particular, is freely soluble in all the aqueous reagents normally used in blood-gas analysis (Nunn, 1958a). For this reason it has not proved possible to use the method of bubble tonometry (Riley, Proemmel and Franke, 1945) for the determination of gas tensions in blood containing nitrous oxide (Nunn, 1958b). This is regrettable as it would have been valuable to determine P_{CO_2} and P_{O_2} at the one operation.

Hitherto most determinations of the arterial P_{CO_2} during anæsthesia have employed the Henderson-Hasselbalch equation, substituting values for the pH and HCO_3^- and assuming values for pK' and the solubility of the CO_2 in the plasma. I have avoided this approach for two main reasons. Firstly, the value for pK' depends on a number of factors—many of which are not constant. It is, therefore, essential that each worker should determine pK' by tonometry under his own experimental conditions and over the range of temperature and pH which he expects to encounter. When this has been done, very accurate determinations of P_{CO_2} may be obtained, but the procedure is laborious and there must be no change in technique once the experimental procedure has been standardized (Severinghaus, Stupfel and Bradley, 1956a). The second objection to the determination of P_{CO_2} by the indirect method is that two separate analytical procedures are required —each with its own problems of execution and maintenance. These difficulties are accentuated when co-ordinating research with an operating theatre schedule and when carrying out the blood analyses single handed in the absence of a technician.

The Interpolation Technique

With CO_2 Content

Determination of the P_{CO_2} may be carried out by interpolation in a plot of P_{CO_2} against either CO_2 content or pH. This approach was used in 1922 by Van Slyke, Austin and Cullen. By tonometry they constructed a dissociation curve and then interpolated the value for the CO_2 content of their original sample to derive the P_{CO_2}. Thereby the only analytical technique required was the determination of the CO_2 content.

With pH

In 1932 Douglas and Havard used a plot of P_{CO_2} against pH to derive P_{CO_2} by interpolation. This plot, however, is a curve and therefore requires a number of points for its definition. Brewin, Gould, Nashat and Neil (1955) drew attention to the fact that a plot of log P_{CO_2} against pH is a straight line over the normal range and can thus be defined by two points only. Astrup (1956) developed a simple apparatus in which the pH of plasma could be measured in the original state and after equilibration at different known CO_2 tensions.

Fig. 1 illustrates a typical analysis of two samples of blood during a clinical study. First the actual pH of the plasma sample is measured. Then the sample is equilibrated with a pair of gas mixtures of known P_{CO_2} which, it is hoped, will bracket the unknown P_{CO_2} of the sample of plasma. The pH is measured after the two equilibrations at known P_{CO_2} and the buffer line of the plasma is drawn. The original pH is then interpolated in this line and so the original P_{CO_2} is derived. Plasma may be equilibrated in 7 minutes and the entire procedure with two equilibrations requires only 20 minutes. Δ log P_{CO_2}/Δ pH is very constant (1·25) and Astrup (1956) has suggested that a single equilibration is sufficient. We have, in practice, carried out two equilibrations and a third if the slope of the line drawn through the first two points appears to be abnormal.

The accuracy of the method for the determination of the

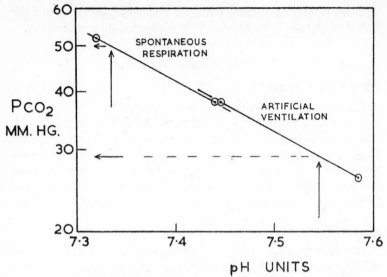

FIG. 1. Plots of P_{CO_2} against pH for two samples of blood. The original pH is shown interpolated to give the P_{CO_2}.

P_{CO_2} of the separated plasma sample depends only upon the accuracy with which differences in pH can be measured. Since the output of a glass electrode is linear, the abscissa may be measured simply in millivolts and it is not necessary to know the true pH. In our case we measure pH difference with a standard deviation of 0·003 pH units and thus it should be possible to measure the P_{CO_2} with 95 per cent confidence limits of $\pm$ 1·5 per cent of the true P_{CO_2}. At 40 mm. Hg, this amounts to $\pm$ 0·6 mm. Hg—an error which compares very favourably with that of other methods for determination of P_{CO_2} of blood.

It is logical to enquire why whole blood should not be used for the construction of a pH/log P_{CO_2} plot. Interpolation would then yield, not the P_{CO_2} of the separated plasma, but the P_{CO_2} of the blood which is, in practice, the value which is almost invariably required. Unfortunately there are a number of objections to the use of whole blood and up to the present time we have not been able to overcome these difficulties. The equilibration of blood at a different P_{CO_2} usually requires a considerably longer time than is necessary for plasma.

Evidence will be presented which suggests that the metabolic acid-base balance of the blood will alter (in spite of the customary precautions to prevent glycolysis) and that the true line of the pH/log P_{CO_2} plot will be displaced during the equilibration. This objection to the use of whole blood might be overcome by equilibration of aliquots of blood simultaneously.

More difficult is the problem of interpolation of the pH of a sample of partially desaturated blood in the pH/log P_{CO_2} plot which would, for practical reasons, have to be prepared with blood fully oxygenated. Oxygenation of the blood will reduce its capacity to carry CO_2 and interpolation would not be valid under these circumstances.

Thus, there appear to be objections to the use of whole blood for the interpolation technique in the presence of desaturation. These objections do not apply to plasma. The metabolic acid-base balance of plasma changes only very slowly after separation and the CO_2 carrying capacity of the plasma is independent of the oxygen tension.

Changes of pH with Separation of Plasma

I feel that there can be little doubt that the interpolation method will give a valid measure of the P_{CO_2} of the sample of saturated plasma. The crux of the matter is therefore how the pH and P_{CO_2} of the separated plasma differs from that of the original blood sample. Two factors may affect the pH of the blood. The first of these is the temperature of separation, and the second is alteration in the fixed acids of the blood after shedding.

If certain data are assumed it is possible to predict the change in pH and P_{CO_2} during separation at different temperatures. Rosenthal (1948) has measured the change of pH when blood and plasma change their temperature under anaerobic conditions. With the exception of the rabbit, in all the species which he investigated, the change of pH with temperature was found to be greater for blood than for plasma. Thus in the human subject the pH of whole blood rises with falling temperature by a mean value of 0·0147 pH units per degree Centigrade. For plasma, the corresponding figure is 0·0118. Thus it would appear that if blood is cooled, and then separated and rewarmed, the pH of the cold-separated plasma will be higher than that of the original blood when both are measured at 38° C. The difference will be approximately 0·003 pH units for every degree Centigrade below 38° C. at which separation was carried out. Under normal laboratory conditions the expected rise resulting from cold separation is of the order of 0·05 pH units which is appreciable, not only for research purposes, but also for general clinical work.

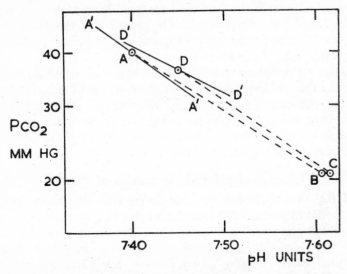

Fig. 2. Diagram to illustrate the theoretical changes in pH and P_{CO_2} which occur when blood is cooled and centrifuged and the plasma rewarmed.

Fig. 2 illustrates the anticipated changes when blood is separated at a temperature of 24° C. In this diagram it is assumed that no changes occur in the level of the fixed acids in the blood during the process of separation. It is also assumed that the partition of CO_2 between red cells and plasma remains constant at different temperatures. This assumption has been verified experimentally by Joffe and Poulton in 1920 and by Severinghaus, Stupfel and Bradley in 1956 (a). It would appear that this constancy of the plasma CO_2 content can only be a fortunate coincidence since most of the factors affecting the partition of CO_2 vary with temperature but apparently in such a manner that the sum of the changes is zero.

The point " A " represents a sample of blood which, at a temperature of 38° C. has a P$_{CO_2}$ of 40 mm. Hg and a pH of 7·400 units. When equilibrated at different tensions of CO_2 the resultant buffer line would be represented by the line " A'A' ". If the blood were cooled anaerobically to 24° C., the data of Rosenthal (1948) would suggest a rise of pH to 7·606 units. On the assumption that the CO_2 content of the plasma remains unchanged, solution of the Henderson-Hasselbalch equation would then indicate a P$_{CO_2}$ of 20·5 mm. Hg—allowance being made for the change in pK' (Severinghaus, Stupfel and Bradley, 1956b). The plot of the cooled blood would then be represented by the point " B ".

If the blood were then separated anaerobically at the new temperature, the pH would appear to have risen by a further 0·008 pH units, due to the effect of removal of the erythrocytes from the vicinity of the glass electrode (point " C "). Rewarming of the plasma to 38° C. for measurement of the pH would then result in a fall in pH. According to Rosenthal's data for plasma the pH of the cold-separated plasma, now rewarmed, would be 7·449, a rise of nearly 0·05 units from the value for the original blood sample. Solution of the Henderson-Hasselbalch equation now indicates a P$_{CO_2}$ of 36·6 mm. Hg (represented by the point " D "), a fall of more than 3 mm. Hg below the value for the original blood sample.

It may be shown experimentally that the buffer line of separated plasma occupies the position " D'D' " with a slope of 1·25. Thus from this hypothetical example it would appear that interpolation of the pH of the separated plasma (" D ") in its own buffer line (" D'D' ") would yield a P$_{CO_2}$ 3·4 mm. Hg below that of the original blood sample. Astrup (1956) recognized this source of error and, since the buffer line of the cold-separated plasma happens to pass very close to the original plot of the blood, recommended the interpolation of the pH of the original blood sample (" A ") in the buffer line of the separated plasma (" D'D' "). This might be expected to yield a value for P$_{CO_2}$ close to that of the whole blood.

This reasoning leans heavily upon three assumptions. Firstly,

D

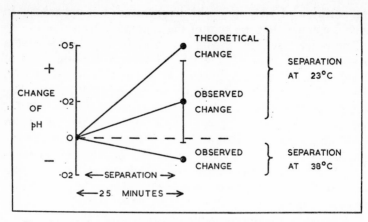

Fig. 3. Observed changes in pH of blood following separation at different temperatures.

TABLE 1. *Difference between pH of blood and cold-separated plasma*

Subject	pH of blood	pH of plasma	pH difference
J.F.N. . . .	7·550	7·590	0·040
	7·329	7·344	0·015
	7·452	7·469	0·017
	7·449	7·466	0·017
	7·562	7·569	0·007
H.C.N. . . .	7·525	7·550	0·025
G.R.G. . . .	7·565	7·595	0·030
J.H.	7·354	7·377	0·023
R.M.	7·410	7·416	0·006
Mean			0·020
S.D. about mean			± 0·011
S.E. of mean			± 0·0037

Note: The mean temperature difference between measurement of pH and separation of blood was 13·5 (range 12·5–15) °C.

that the changes in pH with temperature are in accord with the mean figures of Rosenthal. Secondly, that the CO_2 content of the plasma is independent of temperature. Thirdly, that during separation, no change occurs in the level of the fixed acids of the blood. We shall, however, show that the third assumption was not valid. Fig. 3 illustrates the changes of pH found experimentally when fresh blood was separated at various temperatures. The top line indicates the expected theoretical change on the assumption that the level of fixed acids remains constant. Below that is shown the mean change observed in nine separations carried out between 20 and 25° C. The limits shown correspond to two standard deviations (Table 1). In these instances no precautions were taken to prevent glycolysis and it is probable that an increase in the fixed acids of the blood has partly offset the change of pH due to cold-separation. Below that is shown the decrease in pH of a single sample of blood separated anaerobically at 38° C. This sample contained fluoride and we had expected that no change would occur.

Changes in the Level of Fixed Acids after Shedding

At this stage of the work it became apparent that changes in the level of the fixed acids of the blood were of considerable importance and, furthermore, changes of pH from this cause did not appear to be fully understood. We, therefore, incubated blood anaerobically at 38° C. and measured the change in pH at intervals. Six runs were made without fluoride and six with 25 mg. of sodium fluoride per 10 ml. of blood, the amount recommended by John (1926) and Jørgensen and Astrup (1957). In addition, 2 mg. of heparin were used for each 10 ml. of blood.

Fig. 4 shows the changes in pH which were found with and without fluoride added to normal venous blood. Without fluoride, the pH fell steadily for at least two hours, the mean change being 0·001 pH units per minute. The individual scatter was not great and in only one case did the rate of change decrease during the period of our observations.

With fluoride on the other hand, the change appeared to be not a linear but a quadratic function, with a fall of pH for the first 40 minutes, later followed by a rise. There was, how-

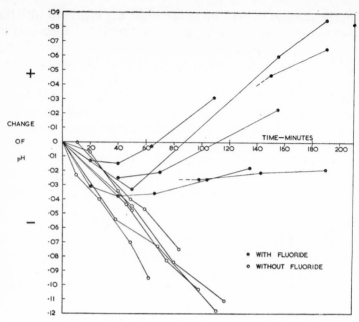

FIG. 4. Observed changes in the pH of blood on standing at 38° C.

ever, quite marked individiual variation. Thus some samples became more alkaline than the original sample within 100 minutes, while in others the blood was still more acid than the original sample after 200 minutes. However in all cases during the second hour the direction of change of pH was towards the acid side. Paired observations were made in four subjects and smoothed curves are shown in Fig. 5.

Certain conclusions can be drawn from this work. Firstly, if the change in pH is measured after a period of two hours the impression may be falsely gained that fluoride can prevent changes in pH. Secondly, since the blood may become relatively alkaline, it is probable that glycolysis is not the only change with which we are concerned. It is in fact known that ammonia may be liberated from adenosine phosphate when blood is allowed to stand. It seems likely that a number of chemical changes may occur and prevention of these changes, other than by reduction of temperature, presents a problem of some difficulty. Thirdly, it is apparent that during the first

40 minutes with which we are particularly concerned, shed blood at 38° C. will develop a metabolic acidosis which cannot be prevented with fluoride. We have not studied the changes during isotonic, as opposed to anaerobic, incubation but it would appear at least possible that, during 30 minutes of equilibration in a tonometer at 38° C., a metabolic acidosis of some 2 to 3 mEq./l. may develop. It is possible that this may explain the discrepancy between the normal arterial

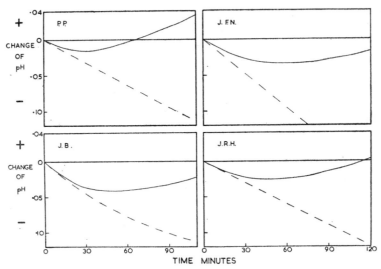

FIG. 5. Observed changes in pH of blood of four subjects on standing at 38° C. The broken lines indicate the changes when there is no addition to the blood while the continuous lines show the effect of the addition of fluoride.

bicarbonate of 25 mEq./l. and the standard bicarbonate found by a number of workers (including myself) to average 22 mEq./l. Finally, it is worthy of note that although the rate of change of pH without fluoride appears to be reasonably constant, with fluoride there is so much scatter that prediction of the change in the individual is impracticable.

Since there appeared to be no prospect of preventing a change in the level of the fixed acids in blood during the first 40 minutes after shedding, it appeared pointless to avoid the change of pH due to cold separation. In fact, since the effect of cold separation was to raise the pH, while changes such as glycolysis lowered the pH, it appeared possible that the two effects might cancel one another. However, since the interaction of the various factors could not be accurately predicted, recourse was made to tonometry to establish the errors in the use of cold-separated plasma for the interpolation technique.

Although this would appear to be a logical approach, the tonometry experiments which we have carried out were in fact commenced 18 months ago when I was not fully aware of these sources of errors. Recently when the effects of cold-separation and glycolysis were more fully understood, we did, in fact, repeat our tonometry experiments, only to find results which were similar to those obtained in our days of relatively greater ignorance.

Accuracy Assessed by Tonometry
Method

Venous blood was used for equilibration and 20 ml. were heparinized and introduced into a 135 ml. tonometer. The tonometer was then rotated on hollow bearings so that a continuous stream of gas could be passed through the tonometer without interrupting the rotation. Equilibration was carried out in a water bath at 38 ($\pm$ 0·1) ° C., the gas stream being obtained from a cylinder whose contents were mixed to an appropriate P_{CO_2}. On four occasions, 70 per cent of nitrous oxide was included in the gas mixture. The blood generally reached equilibrium with the gas in 35 minutes. This was demonstrated by closing both taps and allowing the tonometer to rotate for another five minutes after which period constancy in the pressure within the tonometer indicated the attainment of equilibrium.

Following equilibration, separation of the gas and blood was accomplished at a constant temperature and pressure, by linking the tonometer to a second tonometer completely filled with mercury, so as to form a closed circle (Fig. 6). The connecting tubing was purged with mercury and then, with the second tonometer elevated, the taps were opened to allow the mercury to flow into the first tonometer. When only blood and mercury remained in the first tonometer and the second tonometer contained gas and mercury, the taps were closed and the tonometers separated. This manœuvre was carried out below the surface of the water bath.

The tonometers were then separated and the gas sample analysed by the method of Scholander (1947). In the case of the gas mixtures containing nitrous oxide, the samples were analysed by a modification of Haldane's method (Nunn, 1958a).

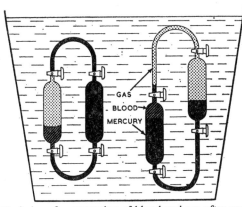

Fig. 6. Technique for separation of blood and gas after equilibration in a tonometer. Temperature and pressure are maintained constant during the manœuvre.

The blood samples were separated at room temperature and the value for the pH of the cold-separated plasma was then measured and interpolated in its own buffer line (Fig. 1). pH was determined at 38° C. by comparison with the buffers recommended by Hitchcock and Taylor (1938). A null reading potentiometric pH meter was used, incorporating a Mullard electrometer valve (type M.E. 1403). The glass electrode assembly was of the type described by Astrup (1956) in which it was possible to equilibrate the plasma samples with various known gas mixtures.

Results

The derived P_{CO_2} of the blood was then compared with the P_{CO_2} of the corresponding gas sample (Fig. 7). The results did not suggest any systematic error and there was only moderate random error about the line of perfect correlation. The mean error of eleven determinations was a blood P_{CO_2} 0·20 mm. Hg higher than that of the gas. The standard error about the mean error was 1·14 mm. Hg giving a standard error of the mean error of 0·34 mm. Hg. The mean error found might therefore be due to chance and has no significance. If it is assumed that there is no significant mean error, the standard

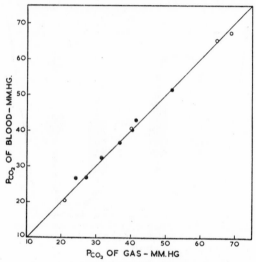

FIG. 7.   Comparison of the measured P_{CO_2} of blood with the P_{CO_2} of gas with which the blood was in equilibrium.

error about zero error is 1·16 mm. Hg. No systematic error appeared to be introduced when nitrous oxide was present in the sample.

Discussion

It must be regarded as another fortunate coincidence that the change in pH and P_{CO_2} due to cold-separation appears to be cancelled by the alteration in the level of fixed acids which takes place between sampling the blood and separating the plasma. Clearly it is essential that the time relations of the technique must be standardized, as the relative absence of error must depend on a certain amount of liberation of fixed acids.

Without doubt the accuracy of the method is adequate for

the assessment of the respiratory acid-base balance of a patient. In fact, under the conditions described, it would appear that the standard deviation of the errors compares favourably with that of bubble tonometry (Shepard and Meier, 1957). The accuracy has been considered acceptable for the determination of the physiological dead space during anæsthesia.

In the light of the new methods for the determination of the arterial P_{CO_2} presented at this symposium, it is appropriate to consider whether there is any place for the interpolation technique using separated plasma. Often, the dominant factors in the choice of a technique for the measurement of arterial blood will be the availability of equipment and the skill and experience of available staff. In this respect the interpolation technique on separated plasma presents certain advantages. It requires only a small outlay in addition to a sensitive pH meter and almost no additional skill is required beyond mastery of the technique for measuring pH.

Summary

There is a tendency for the pH of blood to increase when it is separated at room temperature and is then rewarmed to 38° C. This change is partly offset by the increase in fixed acids which occurs in blood after shedding.

The addition of fluoride to blood alters the nature of the change of pH with time from a linear function to a quadratic function. For the first 40 minutes the pH falls normally; later the pH rises and usually it becomes greater than that of the original blood sample after 2 hours.

These changes due to cold separation and liberation of fixed acids largely cancel each other out and it is therefore possible to determine the P_{CO_2} of blood by the interpolation of pH in a pH/log P_{CO_2} plot on the cold-separated plasma. The accuracy of this method appears to compare favourably with that of other techniques for the determination of P_{CO_2} of blood.

Acknowledgements

I am indebted to Mr. D. W. Hill for the design and construction of the pH meter. It is a pleasure to acknowledge the help received from Miss T. C. Guilfoyle and Miss P. Probst.

REFERENCES

ASTRUP, P. (1956). A Simple Electrometric Technique for the Determination of Carbon Dioxide Tension in Blood and Plasma, Total Content of Carbon Dioxide in Plasma and Bicarbonate Content in " Separated " Plasma at a Fixed Carbon Dioxide Tension (40 mm. Hg). *Scand. J. clin. Lab. Invest.*, **8**, 33.

BREWIN, E. G., GOULD, R. P., NASHAT, F. S., and NEIL, E. (1955). An Investigation of Problems of Acid-base Equilibrium in Hypothermia. *Guy's Hosp. Rep.*, **104**, 177.

DOUGLAS, C. G., and HAVARD, R. E. (1932). The Changes in the CO_2 Pressure and Hydrogen Ion Concentration of the Arterial Blood of Man which are associated with Hyperpnœa due to CO_2. *J. Physiol.*, **74**, 471.

HITCHCOCK, D. I., and TAYLOR, A. C. (1938). The Standardisation of Hydrogen Ion Determinations. II. A Standardisation of the pH Scale at 38° C. *J. Amer. chem. Soc.*, **60**, 2710.

JOFFE, J., and POULTON, E. P. (1920). The Partition of CO_2 between Plasma and Corpuscles in Oxygenated and Reduced Blood. *J. Physiol.*, **54**, 129.

JOHN, H. J. (1926). Preservation and Transportation of Blood for Chemical Study. *Arch. Path. lab. Med.*, **1**, 227.

JØRGENSEN, K., and ASTRUP, P. (1957). Standard Bicarbonate, its Clinical Significance, and a New Method for its Determination. *Scand. J. clin. Lab. Invest.*, **9**, 122.

NUNN, J. F. (1958a). Respiratory Measurements in the Presence of Nitrous Oxide. *Brit. J. Anæsth.*, **30**, 254.

NUNN, J. F. (1958b). Factors affecting the Arterial Carbon Dioxide Tension during Anæsthesia. *Ph.D. thesis. University of Birmingham.*

RILEY, R. L., PROEMMEL, D. D., and FRANKE, R. E. (1945). Direct Method for Determination of O_2 and CO_2 Tensions in Blood. *J. biol. Chem.*, **161**, 621.

ROSENTHAL, T. B. (1948). The Effect of Temperature on the pH of Blood and Plasma *in vitro*. *J. biol. Chem*, **173**, 25.

SCHOLANDER, P. F. (1947). Analyser for Accurate Estimation of Respiratory Gases i n One-half Cubic Centimetre Samples. *J. biol. Chem.*, **167**, 235.

SEVERINGHAUS, J. W., STUPFEL, M., and BRADLEY, A. F. (1956a). Accuracy of Blood pH and P_{CO_2} Determinations. *J. appl. Physiol.*, **9**, 189.

SEVERINGHAUS, J. W., STUPFEL, M., and BRADLEY, A. F. (1956b). Variations of Serum Carbonic Acid pK' with pH and Temperature. *J. appl. Physiol.*, **9**, 197.

SHEPARD, R. H., and MEIER, P. (1957). An Analysis of the Errors of a Bubble Method for Estimation of P_{CO_2} and P_{O_2} in Whole Blood. *J. appl. Physiol.*, **11**, 241.

VAN SLYKE, D. D., AUSTIN, J. H., and CULLEN, G. E. (1922). The Effect of Ether Anæsthesia on the Acid-base Balance of the Blood. *J. biol. Chem.*, **53**, 277.

DISCUSSION

Astrup: With regard to the action of sodium fluoride on the pH we have not found this rise in pH when we added fluoride. Perhaps it is because we have not investigated as closely as Dr. Nunn has. But we are about to reinvestigate it so I will later come back to this problem in a letter to Dr. Nunn. In our hands the equilibration technique has been very satisfactory and I agree with Dr. Nunn that the best of the technique is that we do not need to worry about the pK values and it does not matter so much which buffer we use.

Sykes: I would like to confirm Dr. Nunn's findings on this fluoride effect. I talked to him about it the other day and went back and looked at my original figures. Using 15 milligrams in 10 ml. of blood we did notice this rise in four cases out of six.

Nunn: I am interested that you should get a rise in pH in four cases out of six, as that is the proportion we found. We started this investigation by just measuring at 0 and 160 minutes and we found that four samples became alkaline and two acid. I had no idea how this could possibly have arisen, and it was only later that we went back and took the readings in the intervening time and that it became apparent what had happened.

Ramwell: We obtained similar results with sodium fluoride about two years ago—very similar to what Dr. Nunn has mentioned. We got this sudden jump and thought it was a fault in the pH meter. We went back again and started measuring at the intervening points and found it swinging over on to the alkaline side just as you said, and it is because of that, and also because of the possible changes in the pK of blood, that we stopped using sodium fluoride.

Severinghaus: Are there enough data available to say whether the effect is proportional to the amount of sodium fluoride used?

Nunn: Not to my knowledge.

Chairman: Can anyone answer that question? My impression is that we do not have the data available.

Wynn: What is the supposed action of sodium fluoride? It does not get into the cells where the glycolysis is going on, so I do not think it would be much use theoretically in preventing glycolysis of whole blood. Have we simply used pretty poor reasoning here for many years to prevent glycolysis with a method which theoretically could not be expected to work.

Nunn: To a large extent fluoride does prevent changes in the level of glucose in the blood. However I believe we are wrong in assuming that glycolysis is the only chemical change which can affect the pH of blood on standing. Dr. Severinghaus has some new information on the action of the white cells in this respect.

Severinghaus: My information on the white cells has to do with the fall of oxygen tension and I cannot say that we have done it with pH. In the oxygen electrode the oxygen tension falls fairly rapidly in whole blood, but if you spin the blood slowly and get a white buffy coat, pull off that white buffy coat consisting of white cells and reconstitute the red cells in the plasma and then repeat the experiment the fall of oxygen tension is greatly reduced. We could not determine the real consumption of oxygen by the red cells, so I suppose the white cells are responsible. Now whether that is also related to the pH fall I do not know, and if it were it would be quite likely, I suppose, that the white cells would take up the sodium fluoride and they might inhibit their production of acid or CO_2.

Campbell: I followed Dr. Nunn very closely, but I am afraid I probably missed the punch line. You showed that this method measures the P_{CO_2} in a tonometer very well. Are you also suggesting that the different effects of temperature on separation, and of time on pH, are such that one can always rely on them to cancel out so that you can also measure the P_{CO_2} of blood from the body?

Nunn: Yes, I think that is reasonable. Without fluoride the increase in fixed acids seems to continue unchanged for at least two hours. It is important that the time relations of the procedure should be held constant, so that the interval between drawing the blood and starting centrifuging must be held constant. Obviously, if the blood is carried around in the pocket for some time beforehand, increase in fixed acids will occur which will not be compensated for by the effects of cold separation. We established a routine in which centrifuging started between 5 and 10 minutes after sampling and we kept to that routine throughout the tonometry runs and in the clinical studies as well.

Campbell: I think one of your slides showed that the rate of pH fall varied considerably with different bloods. Do you mean that in those individuals the effect of temperature on CO_2 content also changed in such a way that they cancelled out or did I misunderstand the slide?

Nunn: I did not think that the rates of fall of pH of unfluorided blood showed all that much scatter. In fact, for a biological phenomenon, the results seemed to be very well grouped.

Campbell: If you take some points there, you have up to ·01 difference in a period of 20 seconds don't you?

Nunn: Yes. That corresponds to about 1 millimetre of mercury. Our SD was 1·16. Therefore our 95 per cent confidence limits were about ± 2½ millimetres of mercury.

Campbell: So, allowing for everything, this method, also, is good to ± 2 millimetres of mercury.

Nunn: Yes.

Mattock: When you make your measurements of pH on your separated plasma are they all made after exactly the same time?

Nunn: Not exactly the same. But then changes in pH occurring in the plasma once it is separated are not very marked. I think the important thing is how long elapses between sampling the blood and getting it into the centrifuge.   The centrifuge is run at constant speed.

Ludbrook: May I ride my hobbyhorse again with regard to separated plasma?   You said you assumed that Rosenthal's figures were substantially correct, that the total CO_2 of plasma did not change, and you made the third assumption, which you later corrected, that there was not any glycolysis, or there was not any change in fixed acid content.   Now surely there must be some change in the plasma, otherwise the rates of change of pH with temperature which Rosenthal obtained for whole blood and for plasma will be the same.   You have a very elegant graph there where you corrected for changes of pH due to the presence of red cells, and yet if you follow those lines, you don't end up where you started from.   So there must be some change in the buffer system of the plasma, I would imagine.   What is that change then if it is not a change in total CO_2 content?

Nunn: I cannot tell you that.   I have found this a very difficult point to understand myself.   I imagine Rosenthal measured the change in temperature with considerable accuracy.   I do not see why there should be any difficulty in that and I think the evidence that Severinghaus and others have obtained of the constancy of the plasma CO_2 content at different temperatures is pretty convincing.

Ludbrook: So something must happen.

Nunn: Something must.   I do not know what it is though.

Wynn: Could I ask Dr. Nunn what are his main practical objectives?   That is to say, could he tell us as an anæsthetist what he wants to achieve in the way of biochemical control of his anæsthetized patient?

Nunn: This was for a specific project, which was to measure the physiological dead space during anæsthesia.

Wynn: Why I asked that question was this: if you think in terms of time the Henderson-Hasselbach type of approach, with ordinary apparatus that most people have, is probably a bit quicker than the equilibration technique using the original Astrup method, but not nearly so quick as the new micro Astrup method which, of course, might put the whole of this completely out of business.   But let us assume for the sake of argument that we want to use existing techniques, then I think probably the original Henderson-Hasselbalch type of approach is probably quicker and easier.   Now, the second point is this: as an anæsthetist suppose you want to control ventilation by means of P_{CO_2} measurement. All you would have to do for most cases would be to measure the pH because if, for the sake of argument, you had a patient who was originally in normal acid-base balance then you could assume a figure for his original bicarbonate.   You could, in fact, measure his original bicarbonate at leisure before the anæsthetic.   Then changes in P_{CO_2} are fundamentally going to be related to changes of pH. The superimposition of metabolic acidosis, which is the only metabolic acid-base change, by the way, which can happen significantly during the anæsthetic, should normally be small. You cannot get much in the way of metabolic alkalosis developing during an anæsthetic. In actual fact in most anæsthetics the metabolic acidosis is a very small factor. Two or 3 millimoles of fixed acid produced is about all you normally get unless the patient is grossly anxoæmic. At least, that is my experience. I have not actually tried to apply this method, but I should imagine that for most practical purposes a simple pH estimation would tell the average anæsthetist very quickly, almost immediately, where he wanted to go.

Nunn: Dealing with these points one by one, firstly there is the question of whether one should set up to measure P_{CO_2} by an interpolation technique or by the Henderson-Hasselbalch approach. I would not suggest that one is any better than the other. I think it is largely a matter of inclination, apparatus you have available, the technical help you have available and so on. In my case, I have never been very much good at the Van Slyke and I have found pH very much easier to measure than CO_2 content, so I have a natural inclination towards the interpolation technique from the start. But I am sure if you had a technician who was competent to use a Van Slyke then the Henderson-Hasselbalch approach would be simpler. Now, the question of whether pH change is sufficient to detect changes in the respiratory acid-base balance of the patient. I have no data myself for the change in metabolic acid-base balance during anæsthesia, but Mr. Hobsley I know has, and I believe that quite marked metabolic acidosis may occur surprisingly quickly during anæsthesia, either from respiratory alkalosis or from a respiratory acidosis. As far as the clinical control of a patient is concerned, I myself feel that the end-tidal CO_2 tension is probably quite adequate. One is not concerned with small variations in P_{CO_2}. The clinical problem in anæsthesia is whether there is a gross reduction or a gross elevation of the CO_2 tension and we have found that in normal patients the arterial to end-tidal CO_2 tension difference is of the order of 5 millimetres of mercury, with a standard deviation of 2 or 3. This we feel to be adequate for clinical use, although of course it is no use in emphysematous patients where the difference, on occasions, is found to be as high as 23 millimetres of mercury.

Wynn: Could we ask Mr. Hobsley whether you get a significant metabolic acidosis or alkalosis quickly? I cannot believe the alkalosis. I cannot see how you could get a metabolic alkalosis.

Nunn: I said a metabolic acidosis due to a respiratory alkalosis or a respiratory acidosis.

Hobsley: Well, the extent of the metabolic acidosis which I have found after operation in 24 cases was 2 to 8 millimoles bicarbonate deficit in 14 of 24 operations. In seven of these operations the figure of deficit was of the order of 6 to 8 millimoles bicarbonate—quite high. With regard to how early you can get this developing, I have only just recently been able to transfer my observations to patients under nitrous oxide anæsthesia and I cannot give you a very full answer, but certainly in three patients who were under controlled respiration and had been under controlled respiration for not more than half an hour and had P_{CO_2}'s of about 28 millimetres, the metabolic acidosis was sufficient to entirely compensate the respiratory alkalosis.

Nunn: In other words, it was of the order of 3 or 4 millimoles per litre.

Hobsley: Yes, that is right.

Chairman: Do you know, Mr. Hobsley, in these cases whether the ventilation applied to the patient was in conformity with the ventilation which he should have had to maintain carbon dioxide balance?

Hobsley: I know that no definite attempt was made to correlate the two rates of ventilation. The other interesting thing is that patients who are unassisted as regards their respiration, always have high P_{CO_2}'s, and they do not actually seem to develop very much of a metabolic acidosis at the beginning. I know that you can get a metabolic acidosis as a result of a respiratory acidosis, but I have not actually seen it myself.

Severinghaus: I suppose we are getting rather close to the philosophy of clinical medicine if we decide whether we should be controlling pH or P_{CO_2} and the only answer we have from that in respiratory physiology is to see what happens in the clinical cases in which unanæsthetized people have metabolic acidosis, and of course there is evidence that there is a compensatory respiratory alkalosis or hyperventilation. As Dr. Wynn has suggested, for clinical purposes it might well be more useful to follow pH than to follow P_{CO_2}. Not as an estimate of P_{CO_2}, but for its own use, to keep pH constant. So if there is a respiratory or a metabolic acidosis it would probably be better to produce a respiratory alkalosis to keep the pH at 7·4 anyway.

Astrup: We have found that a metabolic acidosis will develop in a patient who has controlled ventilation. It depends on how low the P_{CO_2} is. If it is very low, about 20, metabolic acidosis will develop rapidly, but if it is above 40 we will have no metabolic acidosis at all. In our opinion the mechanism seems to be that the kidney will excrete base, keeping the pH normal.

Wynn: That is in an unanæsthetized patient, of course?

Chairman: That is just the point I was going to raise. Your healthy subject is one thing and your anæsthetized surgical patient possibly suffering from all manner of metabolic disturbances—kidney damage, perhaps, in some cases, and from anæmia and dehydration—is quite another. I do not think we have very much information on how quickly in fact metabolic compensation can be produced in surgical patients who are physically abnormal in various ways. Perhaps the work that Mr. Hobsley is doing (when it comes to fruition) will throw more light on that.

Wynn: I would like to say that urinary excretion is tremendously important. The observations that I have done in the past—they have not been very many or recent—suggest that renal compensation to these changes is practically abolished during anæsthesia.

Hobsley: The trouble is, of course, the collection of urinary specimens during anæsthesia, isn't it? And it may be possible to approach this from the other side of the renal barrier. I have just been thinking along the lines of what is the acid in the blood that accounts for this metabolic acidosis. What is the non-buffer anion that accumulates in the blood? Because there must be one.

Severinghaus: Certainly, one of the causes of this metabolic acidosis is tissue ischæmia or anoxia. We see for example after inflow occlusion for cardiac surgery that there may be a drop in CO_2 content of 3 or 4 millimoles within 5 or 10 minutes.

Hobsley: Have you any information about lactic acid levels, Dr. Severinghaus?

Severinghaus: I have not done them. Some others have. They have been found to be greatly elevated of course after shock or hæmorrhage and in tissue anoxia.

Nunn: Professor Neil, I think, has shown that after hypothermia and circulatory occlusion the decrease in the fixed acids can be accounted for almost entirely by increases in lactic and pyruvic acid.

VIII. ULTRA-MICRO-METHOD—FOR DETERMINING pH, P_{CO_2} AND STANDARD BICARBONATE IN CAPILLARY BLOOD

Poul Astrup

Department of Clinical Chemistry, Rigshospitalet, Copenhagen, Denmark

BEFORE speaking about the methodological problems I should like to mention the definitions used by us for the different disturbances in acid-base metabolism, and further evaluate what in my opinion must be considered as relevant values for characterizing the disturbances both qualitatively and quantitatively.

Definitions

We define an acidosis as a condition with decreased pH of blood and an alkalosis as a condition with increased pH of blood.

A respiratory acidosis is defined as a acidosis due to an increase of P_{CO_2}, and a respiratory alkalosis as an alkalosis due to a decrease of P_{CO_2} in arterial blood. A metabolic acidosis is defined as an acidosis due to a decrease of standard bicarbonate, and a metabolic alkalosis as an alkalosis due to an increase of standard bicarbonate.

Relevant Values for Characterizing Non-respiratory Disturbances

The term standard bicarbonate deserves an explanation. The word standard should signify that the bicarbonate has to be measured under standardized conditions for expressing the non-respiratory side of the acid-base metabolism only. The standardized conditions must be a fixed P_{CO_2} and a fixed oxygenation of hæmoglobin, so that the influence of respiration on the acid-base content of the blood can be eliminated. We have chosen to measure with the hæmoglobin completely oxygenated and at a P_{CO_2} of 40 mm. Hg and at 38° C. If, with these conditions fulfilled, the pH of blood is measured, the Henderson-Hasselbalch equation

$$pH = 6\cdot11 + \log \frac{HCO_3^-}{P_{CO_2} \times 0\cdot03}$$

will give the standard bicarbonate directly by inserting the found value for pH and 40 for the P_{CO_2}. Standard bicarbonate can thus be defined as the concentration of bicarbonate in plasma, which may be separated from the cells with the hæmoglobin completely oxygenated, at a P_{CO_2} of 40 mm. Hg and at a temperature of 38° C.

However, often two other quantities are measured, namely the total content of CO_2 of plasma and the CO_2-combining power. Total-CO_2 is defined as the total content of CO_2 in plasma separated from the cells at the actual P_{CO_2}. The CO_2-combining power is defined as the content of the total CO_2 in plasma, which is separated from the cells at the actual P_{CO_2} and then equilibrated with carbon dioxide at a P_{CO_2} of 40 mm. before the measuring.

Let us see what becomes of the three quantities: total-CO_2, CO_2-combining power and standard bicarbonate if one measures on the same blood sample. We take a blood sample from a normal person into an Erlenmeyer flask. We mix it well and make sure that the blood is uniform. We then divide it into six tubes (Fig. 1). In tubes 1, 2 and 3 we oxygenate the hæmoglobin completely, whereas in tubes 4, 5 and 6 we reduce the hæmoglobin completely. Hereafter we equilibrate tubes 1 and 4 to a P_{CO_2} of 20 mm., tubes 2 and 5 to a P_{CO_2} of 40 mm., and tubes 3 and 6 to a P_{CO_2} of 80 mm.

The previously uniform blood is now divided into six portions, in which have varied only the P_{CO_2} and the oxygenation of the hæmoglobin. We have thus produced the extremes of the different conditions which can be induced by changes in the respiration. If we now determine the three quantities for each of the six samples just mentioned we will arrive at the figures appearing in Table 1. You will see that both for the total CO_2 and the CO_2 combining power, the figures vary considerably, while the standard bicarbonate is exactly the same in all samples. This confirms that standard bicarbonate is the proper thing to measure, when one wants to standardize

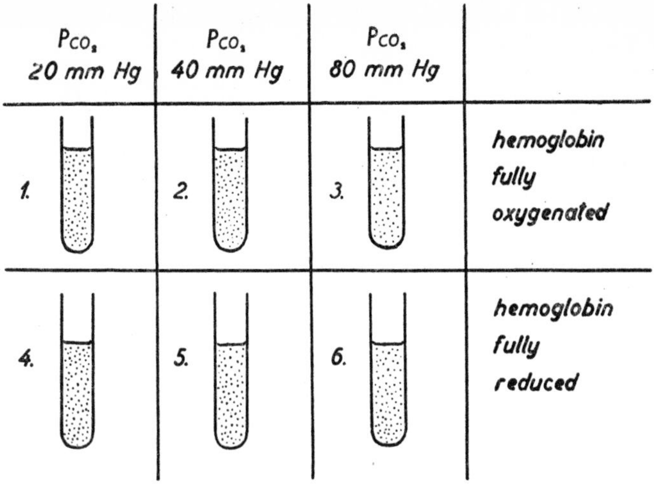

Fig. 1. Tubes containing blood (from the same blood pool) at different P_{CO_2} and with the hæmoglobin fully oxygenated and fully reduced, respectively.

the influence of the respiration and determine the metabolic component.

For further evaluation of the quantitative relations it is necessary to know the total amount of surplus acid or surplus base, which is contained per litre blood at a given concentration of standard bicarbonate. This amount, which can be

TABLE 1. *The content of total CO_2, CO_2 combining power and standard bicarbonate in plasma from the same blood sample at varying P_{CO_2} and varying oxygen saturation (in mEq./1).*

	P_{CO_2} 20 mm. Hg	P_{CO_2} 40 mm. Hg	P_{CO_2} 80 mm. Hg	
Total CO_2 . .	16·8	22·2	30·0	fully oxy-
CO_2 combining power	18·0	22·2	27·5	genated
Standard bicarbonate	21·0	21·0	21·0	blood
Total CO_2 . .	19·6	25·7	34·8	Fully
CO_2 combining power	21·0	25·7	31·9	reduced
Standard bicarbonate	21·0	21·0	21·0	blood

signified by Δ acid-base, can be found easily by the method described later on.

When Δ acid-base is known, the total amount of surplus acid or surplus base in the extracellular space can be found by using the formula:

$$0\cdot30 \times \text{body weight in kg} \times$$
$$\Delta \text{ acid-base per litre blood.}$$

This amount directly corresponds to the amount of sodium bicarbonate (or ammonium chloride) which has to be given to a patient to promote a normal value for standard bicarbonate. The formula has been evaluated by Mellemgaard and Astrup (1959) by studying the alterations following rapid intravenous infusion of sodium bicarbonate to normal individuals.

The Theoretical Background for the Electrometric Determination of the Relevant Values

The theoretical background for the electrometric determinations of P_{CO_2} and of standard bicarbonate is, that graphs showing the relations between log P_{CO_2} and pH are straight lines, (shown experimentally by Neill et al. (1955) and Astrup (1956)). By equilibrating a blood sample at two CO_2-tensions and measuring the pH values, two points of the corresponding graph are determined, and consequently so is the whole curve for the sample in question (Fig. 2). If the actual pH of the blood sample is known then the actual P_{CO_2} can easily be found.

The standard bicarbonate can be derived from the pH-value corresponding to $P_{CO_2} = 40$ mm. Hg on the log P_{CO_2}/pH curve found. The abscissa in Fig. 2 shows pH values and standard bicarbonate values as well.

The slope of a log P_{CO_2}/pH curve depends on the buffer capacity of the blood. This can be seen from Fig. 3, which shows log P_{CO_2}/pH curves for samples with varying content of hæmoglobin, derived from the same blood pool by adding or subtracting plasma.

If to such samples the same amount of acid or base is added, and then new log P_{CO_2}/pH curves are determined, the points of intersection form a curve. This curve, which has been worked

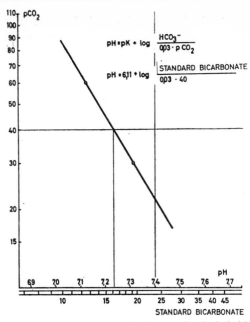

FIG. 2. Graph relating P_{CO_2} and pH of a sample of whole blood.

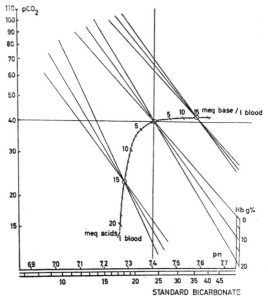

FIG. 3. Variations in the slope of graphs relating P_{CO_2} and pH in samples of whole blood with different content of hæmoglobin.

out by Siggaard Andersen and Engel (1959) thus indicates the amount of surplus acid or surplus base found in the blood.

The curve in the upper left corner in Fig. 4 expresses the content of Buffer Base (B_B) according to the definition of Singer and Hastings (1948). B_B is the sum of cations corresponding to the buffer anions. In my opinion the use of this value is inappropriate because the word is used for cations, thus not following the modern definitions of acid and base,

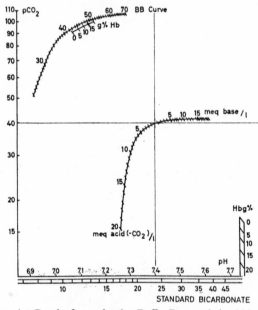

FIG. 4. Graphs for evaluating Buffer Base and Δ acid-base.

and further because it includes the cations corresponding to the hæmoglobin anions. A patient with a low concentration of hæmoglobin can have an abnormal B_B without alterations in the acid-base metabolism at all.

Problems concerning this point are further discussed elsewhere (Astrup, Jørgensen, Siggaard Andersen and Engel, 1959).

The conclusion is that exact measurement of blood pH at the actual P_{CO_2} and at two known values for P_{CO_2} will allow the calculations of all relevant blood data concerning the acid-base status.

Electrometric Micro Methods

One of the purposes of the analytical work in my laboratory during the last few years has been to work out methods for the electrometric determinations of the quantities referred to.

Macromethods were first developed: pH was measured anaerobically at 38° C. in a special chamber (Astrup and Schrøder, 1956), P_{CO_2} was measured in the same chamber by the equilibration technique and by using plasma separated anaerobically from the cells (Astrup, 1956). Finally standard bicarbonate was measured using the equilibration technique on whole blood (Jørgensen and Astrup, 1957). For these analyses about 10 ml. blood had to be used.

As microanalyses for pH, P_{CO_2} and standard bicarbonate on capillary blood were urgently required for use as bedside tests, we decided to try to develop such methods. We had success in our work and about one month ago we perfected the method which I am now going to describe. It will be published by Siggaard Andersen, Engel, Jørgensen and Astrup in the *Scandinavian Journal of Clinical and Laboratory Investigation* in 1959. As other micromethods do not include

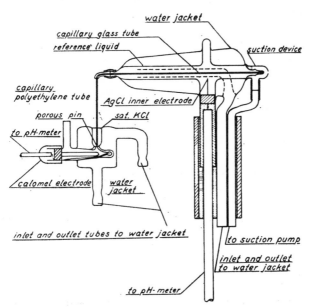

Fig. 5. Capillary glass electrode for measuring blood pH.

determinations of all the relevant values, I shall not take the time now to mention these, but I shall possibly revert to them in the discussion if required.

Electrodes. Our first object was to find a microelectrode, which could measure pH of blood anaerobically and at 38° C. We tried different types but very soon it became obvious that the electrode described by Sanz (1958) might have the qualities for which we were looking. The Danish firm Radiometer had for some time worked with the same problem, and with our co-operation the electrode shown in Fig. 5 was developed. The electrode corresponds in principle to Sanz's electrode. It consists of a capillary glass tube which has been fused into a glass tube containing the reference-liquid. It might be mentioned that the capillary glass tube can be renewed. An AgCl electrode is used as inner electrode. The electrode is moreover sealed into a water jacket made of glass with inlet and outlet pipes contained in the handle of the electrode. The temperature of the water should be kept at 38° C. The water contains about 1 per cent sodium chloride for shielding purposes. At one end of the electrode a short polyethylene tube is fixed. This protects the capillary tube and is also used as a holder for a longer capillary tube made of polyethylene. This tube is interchangeable to avoid contamination from one patient to another. The point of the tube is placed in the centre of the drop of blood when filling the electrode. For this 20–25 μl. is used. A suction device at the opposite end is connected with a suction pump through the handle of the electrode. When the electrode is held by hand the thumb can easily be placed over the small hole in the suction device, and thus suction is established through the capillary tube.

The reference electrode is a thermostatted, saturated calomel electrode. The electrode half cell is connected with a little pool of saturated potassium chloride solution through a porous pin.

The glass electrode is portable and constructed for measurements on capillary blood taken directly at the bedside. Before measuring, the capillary tube is filled with buffer solution (pH 7·360 at 38° C.) by suction. The electrode is then placed in a holder so that the point of the polyethylene tube is submerged in the saturated potassium chloride. The meter is adjusted to show the pH of the buffer. Then distilled water is sucked through the capillary tube, and the electrode is ready for filling with blood and the subsequent measuring, which is carried out in the same way as the buffer adjustment. Each measurement takes only about half a minute, and the blood should be sucked away with buffer solution, immediately the result has ben read.

The electrode is extremely stable and the standard deviation when determining blood pH is only 0·006 pH units. The pH-meter used was Radiometer PHM 22 with extra scale between pH 6·00 and 8·00.

Equilibration. For the equilibration of small amounts of blood with two CO_2-tensions a special equilibration chamber was constructed (Fig. 6). The tubes are built into a water jacket, kept at

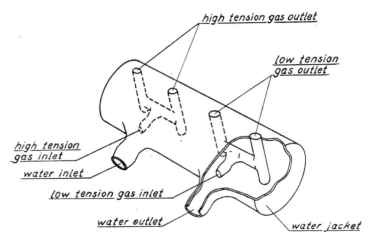

FIG. 6. Chamber for equilibrating small blood samples.

38° C., and the gas mixture (O_2-CO_2-mixture from two cylinders) is led to them through outlet tubes (see Fig. 6). In this way it is possible to maintain the temperature of the gas at 38° C. The gas is saturated with water vapour at 38° C. by bubbling it through N/10 lactic acid in the humidifier shown in Fig. 7. Thus the volume of small amounts of blood kept at the bottom of the equilibration tubes is not changed. We have carefully measured the temperature in the whole system (electrodes, chamber etc.) and found it to be within 38° C. $\pm$ 0·2°.

The equilibration chamber is suspended, freely movable about its longitudinal axis, in two ball bearings. A motor provided with an eccentric axle makes it possible to vibrate the aggregate vigorously. During this process the blood, placed in the bottom of the equilibration chamber as a little drop, forms a thin film on the sides and diffusion equilibrium

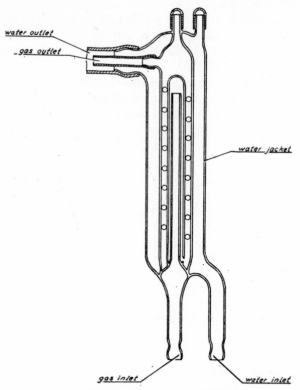

FIG. 7. Humidifier for saturating gas with water vapour.

is reached in approximately one minute. No hæmolysis occurs. If the motor is stopped the blood will again form a drop at the bottom of the chamber and from here it can be sucked up into the electrode.

The whole arrangement, together with the cylinders, can be mounted on a small mobile table and thus made portable so that the analyses can be done on capillary blood as a bedside test.

Procedure. The blood is taken from ear or finger. About 25 μl. blood for actual pH is obtained anaerobically by sucking up from the centre of the drop of blood. No anticoagulants are used. The pH is then measured. Thereafter about 80–90 μl. blood is obtained by suction (anaerobic conditions unnecessary) in a plastic tube, containing a little heparin, and about 40 μl. is transferred to two of the equilibration tubes for equilibration at a low and a high P_{CO_2} respectively (about 30 and 60 mm. Hg). After three minutes the pH is measured in the two samples. The whole measurement can thus be finished within five minutes.

If it is desired to postpone the equilibration, some lithium fluoride can be added to the blood in order to prevent glycolysis.

Calculations. The calculation is then carried out according to the principle described before (Fig. 8). Of course, the same log P_{CO_2}/pH-curve can ordinarily be used for hours when the

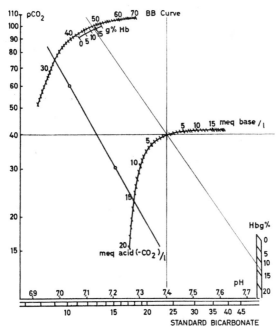

FIG. 8. Graph showing calculations of Δ acid-base or Buffer Base of a blood sample.

purpose is to follow the P_{CO_2} in a patient where no alterations in the non-respiratory acid-base metabolism are expected to occur.

If the oxygen saturation in the capillary blood is not 100 per cent a correction can be introduced. For each gram unsaturated hæmoglobin per 100 ml. blood the log P_{CO_2}/pH-curve must be transferred 0·005 pH units to the left to obtain a correct value for P_{CO_2}. In most cases this correction will be unnecessary.

Accuracy. Altogether the uncertainty of the electrometric measurements is quite small. The value of actual pH as well as that of pH after equilibration is found to vary within $\pm$ 0·006 pH. If the CO_2 tensions of the gas in the cylinders are 60 mm. Hg and 30 mm. Hg respectively, our pH_{40} value will vary within $\pm$ 0·004 pH. After this the standard bicarbonate determination will be within $\pm$ 1 per cent. It is a little more difficult to state the error on the P_{CO_2} determination as it depends on the log P_{CO_2}/pH curve as well as on the value of the actual P_{CO_2} as compared to the P_{CO_2} at which the equilibration takes place. If the P_{CO_2} is between the two reference tensions, the error will be approximately $\pm$ 0·5 per cent, and if it is outside, within $\pm$ 3 per cent. To this must be added the systematic errors due to variations in temperature, in buffer pH and in the tensions in the two cylinders. However, these errors are negligible if due care is taken.

We are hoping that this method, which I have now described, will be useful for clinical work, especially in anesthesiology, in heart-lung surgery, and in investigating heart-lung diseases, and other diseases affecting the respiratory system. We also hope that it will be useful for the qualitative and quantitative evaluation of problems concerning the non-respiratory acid-base metabolism.

REFERENCES

ANDERSEN, O. SIGGAARD, and ENGEL, K. (1959). *Scand. J. clin. Lab. Invest. In press.*

ANDERSEN, O. SIGGARD, ENGEL, K., JØRGENSEN, K., and ASTRUP, P. (1959). *Scand. J. clin. Lab. Invest. In press.*

ASTRUP, P. (1956). A Simple Electrometric Technique for the Determination of Carbon Dioxide Tension in Blood and Plasma, Total Content of Carbon Dioxide in Plasma, and Bicarbonate Content in

" Separated " Plasma at a Fixed Carbon Dioxide Tension (40 mm. Hg). *Scand. J. clin. Lab. Invest.*, **8**, 33.

ASTRUP, P., JØRGENSEN, K., ANDERSEN, O. SIGGAARD, and ENGEL, K. (1959). *In press.*

ASTRUP, P., and SCHRØDER, S. (1956). Apparatus for Anaerobic Determination of the pH of Blood at 38° C. *Scand. J. clin. Lab. Invest.*, **8**, 30.

BREWIN, E. G., GOULD, R. P., NASHAT, F. S., and NEIL, E. (1955). An Investigation of Acid-base Equilibrium in Hypothermia. *Guy's Hosp. Rep.*, **104**, 177.

JØRGENSEN, K., and ASTRUP, P. (1957). Standard Bicarbonate, its Clinical Significance, and a New Method for its Determination. *Scand. J. clin. Lab. Invest.*, **9**, 122–132.

MELLEMGAARD, K., and ASTRUP, P. (1959). *Scand. J. clin. Lab. Invest. In press.*

SANZ, M. C. (1957). Ultramicro Methods and Standardization of Equipment of Clinical Chemistry, **3**, 406.

SINGER, RICHARD B., and HASTINGS, A. BAIRD (1948). An Improved Clinical Method for the Estimation of Disturbances of the Acid-base Balance of Human Blood. *Medicine (Baltimore)*, **22**, 223.

DISCUSSION

Chairman: Dr. Astrup's method has impressed us all, I am quite sure, by its elegance, and obviously if one can use capillary blood it makes it very much easier than having to go through all the rigmarole of arterial puncture. This obviously raises the question: how reliable is capillary blood as an estimate of arterial blood?

Astrup: We have not compared it yet, but in the literature it is said that there are only very small differences. I don't know.

Chairman: This depends, obviously, on adequate warming of the ear or of the finger. Dr. Severinghaus, would you like to discuss Dr. Astrup's paper?

Severinghaus: No! I think it is a very wonderful piece of work. I must only compliment you on an extremely fine presentation. That nomograph is very ingenious, the one with all the curves on it. Is it going to be published?

Astrup: Yes. It is going to be published. I worked on it together with my co-workers. I must mention their names: Siggaard Andersen, Engel and Jørgensen, and in the coming numbers of the *Scandinavian Journal of Clinical & Laboratory Investigation* all our work will appear.

Severinghaus: It certainly seems to me that this approach greatly simplifies this entire problem of acid-base balance for clinical medicine and, as far as I can see, for research work too. And if one is not happy about capillary blood drops one can always get arterial blood and put it into the apparatus and still get the right answer. And the fact that you can do it all within one or two minutes of equilibration eliminates the problems of the glycolysis; you do it with dried heparin so you do not have so much problem of dilution. You do not have to heparinize the blood you put in the capillary originally. It is a beautiful method.

Wynn: The clinical problems of acid-base balance and its control have, as far as I know, baffled clinicians for 30 years. Peters and Van Slyke about 30 years ago described nearly all the basic concepts we have heard today. We have merely elaborated upon them. Nevertheless, in clinical work these concepts have just not caught on. Perhaps this is our opportunity, and if we all press in one direction we might get it into clinical work. This is something I personally am going to think about a great deal when I have got Dr. Astrup's data in front of me and can check them against the pathological case. I think it works beautifully in the normal. I am not sure about these P_{CO_2}/pH plots in pathological situations in which you find not only anoxæmia, but a variety of metabolic and respiratory disorders at the same time. The main point in my mind at the moment is that it is not the acid-base balance of blood which we want to understand, it is the acid-base balance of the body. By taking out some blood—and when it is only 20 to 30 microlitres it is an extraordinarily small fraction of the whole patient—and equilibrating it in the way Dr. Astrup describes, I am just wondering whether we are superimposing our facts into our analysis of the acid-base situation in the whole patient. After all, that type of approach has, I think, been rather inhibitory in the past. Books have been written about the acid-base balance of the blood. Little has been written, to my knowledge, on the acid-base balance of the body, and more than half the buffering occurs inside the cells, not of the blood, but of the general tissue cells. What happens to red cells in equilibration, and what measures you then get of standard bicarbonate in a small sample of blood, may be rather different if you apply your equilibration to the whole patient. If you could equilibrate the whole patient, of course, and show that your standard bicarbonate was 15 or 20 or 12 mM/1, then I personally would go to your very elegant equation $0\cdot3 \times$ body weight $\times \Delta$ standard bicarbonate with a good deal more confidence than I can at the moment pretend that I have. If I have made everything very confusing I apologize. The presentation of your method has been very fascinating to us all and if we can all accept it, then I hope we will all press for it in clinical work. But just to make myself quite clear, I believe that you have still got to show that putting your patient in a tonometer gives you the same result as putting a small fraction of your patient's blood in the tonometer.

Chairman: Thank you Dr. Wynn. Well here we see history repeating itself in the transfer of attention from the macrocosm to the microcosm. In physics we started off with molecules and we are getting down to atoms, to electrons and their various reactions. The same sort of transfer seems to be taking place in biochemistry in that we are bringing analytical techniques to bear on ever smaller quantities. We have to reckon with temperatures, of course. Two years ago all biologists could entertain the concept of body temperature quite happily; that is no longer so. We are now becoming increasingly aware of the fact that there are gradients of temperature in the body, and this too has its bearing on the aspects of biochemistry which we are considering.

Campbell: Could I ask, Sir, while we have this assembly of talent, if there is agreement as to whether a log P_{CO_2}/pH graph would be the best thing for us all to try and persuade doctors to think of, or whether something like a bicarbonate pH diagram is easier?

Astrup: Yes. We have worked over the whole problem very carefully and discussed it for months and have now decided to keep the blood P_{CO_2}/pH diagram. We think it is the easiest way to visualize all relevant values at least for the clinicians. We have drawn other types of diagrams and have tried them on doctors, but they all say that this is the easiest graph to understand, because you get everything you want. Laboratory technicians also prefer the blood P_{CO_2}/pH diagram because they directly use the P_{CO_2} and pH values. May I answer Dr. Wynn by showing two slides. Here (Fig. 9) are our results of infusing sodium bicarbonate intravenously. We gave 167 milli-equivalents very rapidly which caused the standard bicarbonate to rise as indicated. In 10 to 15 to 20 minutes the blood values decreased rather rapidly. We think that at the point where the decrease becomes slower the whole extracellular space has been filled up with sodium bicarbonate. An important thing is to know the equilibration between the extracellular space and the intracellular space and we have found that

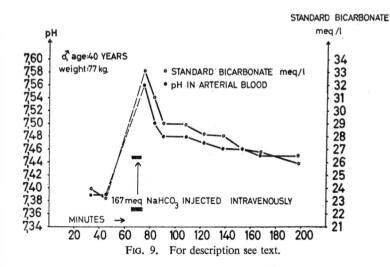

Fig. 9. For description see text.

it varies from patient to patient. As far as I can see, the only thing to do is to give a patient sodium bicarbonate or ammonium chloride corresponding respectively to the surplus or deficit of acid in the extracellular space. As far as I know it is an old clinical experience that some patients with acidosis need enormous amounts of sodium bicarbonate to reach normal blood values. Others do not. Table 2 is from a patient with a brainstorm thrombosis. He had a respiratory acidosis and very soon developed acute renal failure. His pH values were determined with our old method, not the micro method or we would have had more values. The total

TABLE 2. *pH, total CO_2 and standard bicarbonate in plasma from a patient with respiratory acidosis and incipient metabolic acidosis.*

Date	a/v-blood	pH	total CO_2 mM	P_{CO_2} mm. Hg	Standard bicarbonate mN	O_2 saturation
19. 12. .	a	7·36	28·3	50	23·4	70
20. 12. .	a	7·32	28·3	56	23·9	96
21. 12. .	a	7·22	30·0	74	22·9	91
22. 12. .	a	7·37	23·0	39	20·9	86
23. 12. .	a	7·27	23·2	50	18·8	71

CO_2 is absolutely within the normal limits. We separate it into the P_{CO_2} and the standard bicarbonate. As you see, on most days the patient had a respiratory acidosis. The first day he had a very low oxygen saturation of his hæmoglobin and that was the cause of the development of the renal failure. His standard bicarbonate on the first two days was about the same and then it decreased and that is because he had no diuresis at all. Consequently his fixed acids were retained in the body and this is shown by the fall in standard bicarbonate. If you had not separated the total CO_2 into the two values here you would not have seen what was happening in the patient. I hope that is an answer to Dr. Wynn.

Chairman: The point that Dr. Campbell made is a very important one, and it would be gratifying if we could all agree upon what is the most desirable method of presentation, and what sort of diagram we should have. At the moment there is considerable confusion about the best way of presenting these things. Perhaps Dr. Nunn has some observations on that.

Nunn: First of all, I want to say how tremendously impressed I am with Dr. Astrup's technique. We have always regarded the problem of ultra-rapid equilibration of whole blood as insoluble and it was quite a shock to realize how easily it could be done. The first question I want to raise on this is the difference in CO_2 capacity of oxygenated and reduced blood and it is a great pity that there is this possibility of error, dependent on the hæmoglobin saturation. It would be interesting if one could get round that problem in some way. It would also be interesting to know the accuracy of this method based on tonometry. One can calculate the error based on considerations of the power of discrimination of the pH meter. But that is not the only source of error. Then there is the problem of how to present metabolic imbalance quantitatively. There are a number of possible methods. There is the total CO_2 content: there is alkali reserve or CO_2 combining power: there is the buffer base: there is the standard bicarbonate: there is the pH/bicarbonate plot: there is the pH/log P_{CO_2} plot. There are six methods of reporting metabolic imbalance and it would seem to me that here has been one of the troubles. People are just not sure which to adopt and consequently have stuck to the old Peters and Van Slyke method of measuring the alkali reserve which, I should say, is probably carried out in some 95 per cent of hospitals in this country. This is based on a concept which is, I think you can say, faulty and, as practised, the technique is also faulty. Equilibration is done at the wrong temperature and so on. Of the graphical methods of presentation, which plot would be the most suitable to adopt, I think, must depend to a large extent on what you are measuring. The pH/bicarbonate plot is advantageous if one is measuring pH and bicarbonate which are the two most convenient parameters to measure. But in Dr. Astrup's case when he is measuring the pH and the P_{CO_2} directly then the pH/log P_{CO_2} plot would appear to be advantageous. Also, if I understood him correctly, it has the further advantage that the hæmoglobin level is given by the slope of the line and the metabolic acid-base balance by the intersept of the line. The last question I would like to ask him is on a point I raised in my paper: can he explain how it is that we all seem to get a standard bicarbonate of about 22 milliequivalents per litre, whereas the normal bicarbonate is about 25? This problem arose when we tried to prepare a normal Davenport diagram and we found we could not reconcile different people's work.

Astrup: Our normal values compare very well with the values found by Asmussen and Nielsen. I do not know if anyone knows them. They have done a lot of work on arterial blood and I have discussed it with Nielsen and we agreed that our normal values are very close to their values of about 23 milliequivalents per litre. To obtain the total CO_2 you have to add 1·2 milliequivalents resulting in between 24 and 25 milliequivalents. If the actual P_{CO_2} is higher than 40 you will get still higher values for total CO_2.

Campbell: Well, in that case I will have to put the question the other way round. What is wrong with everybody who measures the plasma CO_2 content with a Van Slyke? I have never studied it formally, but I think there are data in the literature which suggest that the average normal value is about 24–25 mM/l and I have studied a considerable number of normal people and that is where they all seem to fall. What is wrong with us? The technique incidentally is that you take the blood, separate the plasma anaerobically and determine the CO_2 content in a Van Slyke by the method of Van Slyke and Neill—why do we get 3 milliequivalents more than we ought to?

Nunn: And also Singer and Hastings.

Campbell: And Singer and Hastings. Why do we do that? Where do we create this CO_2 from?

Astrup: Well, if you measure at exactly 40 mm. Hg I do not think there will be any difference and you must remember that in the Van Slyke apparatus you measure the total CO_2. You then have to add 1·2 milliequivalents to the standard bicarbonate to get the total CO_2 of plasma.

Campbell: Yes. But the difference is not 1·2. The difference is of the order of 3 or 4.

Astrup: I do not think so.

Nunn: In our experience, it is.

Astrup: Is it so much?

Severinghaus: What is your mean?

Astrup: Well, we found it to be 21·7. I think that is a little too low. Possibly it should be between 22 and 23. We are going now to determine it with the new method.

Wynn: Perhaps the answer is in the numbers already given us. Your original work was done with an equilibration taking half an hour in which a certain amount of acid metabolites were being produced, whereas the Van Slyke method is done virtually instantaneously. If we had equilibrated our blood for half an hour and then Van Slyked it we would probably get figures very similar to yours.

Astrup: I do not remember that Van Slyke has published values for arterial blood. He has taken them from the literature. At least, the values he has published in his book.

Campbell: Asmussen and Nielsen's was also tonometer blood wasn't it?

Astrup: No. They have done it on arterial blood in normal persons.

Campbell: Just take it straight and put it in a Van Slyke?

Astrup: Yes. After centrifuging it at the actual P_{CO_2} to obtain plasma.

Hobsley: It is just a question then of the complete oxygenation, complete saturation of the blood which you achieve when you do your standard bicarbonate, as distinct from the fact that in clinical practice you very rarely get P_{O_2}'s above 80 millimetres of mercury, or 85 say. I wonder if that makes a difference?

Astrup: It can make a difference, of course.

Hobsley: And as you say, it makes a difference to those standard bicarbonates as distinct from the bicarbonate level that is actually present, and I wonder if that may not be responsible for these discrepancies.

Severinghaus: A P_{O_2} of 80 is still 95 per cent saturated.

Hobsley: Yes. But it is a question of whether it affects the buffering power of the red cell.

Severinghaus: Well, that is only a 5 per cent difference. Now, I understood from what you said that you can correct this desaturation by moving over your pH scale ·005 per gramme of hæmoglobin. Would that give you the complete picture even on reduced venous blood?

Astrup: Yes. If you take arterial blood and measure the pH at the same tension, and if you then reduce the hæmoglobin completely you get a rise in the pH of about 0·06 pH units: between 0·06 and 0·07.

Severinghaus: At the same P_{CO_2}?

Astrup: The same P_{CO_2}, yes. We have found it and Van Slyke has found it.

Chairman: Well, it looks as though there is still some discrepancy, some difference which is unaccounted for by two different sets of workers. I suppose the only way to resolve this would be to put representatives of the two schools side by side at the same bench and give them the same sample of blood to analyse. The difference, however, I think comes down to something pretty small—perhaps not more than 2 millimoles.

Campbell: I am sorry to say I have not studied this formally. I think that the normal CO_2 content with arterial plasma measured in a Van Slyke is in a quite narrow range. I think it is probably only something of the order of 24 to 27. Well, this is 3. The difference between that range and Dr. Astrup's range is 3, so we have a difference which is big compared with the range. So I think we want to try and account for it if we are going to compare data. Now, I am sorry I cannot give you the percentages. All I can say is that I have over the course of years measured the arterial CO_2 content of a considerable number of people, and my memory is that it is always above 22.

Astrup: It is above. I agree. Perhaps our value 6·11 for pK is too high. If it was 0·02–0·03 lower the results would be almost identical.

Campbell: And either we are wrong or some loss of CO_2 occurred in your early data. Possibly when you do it in such a way that time does not enter into it, you will in fact find the standard bicarbonate is higher?

Astrup: I can say that for the last two years, we have measured standard bicarbonate as a routine in my hospital. We now never determine the total CO_2 or the CO_2 combining power, and we have about 30 analyses per day and I am quite sure that the average is about 23 milliequivalents.

Hobsley: May I revert to another point in the very important question of the best way of presenting the results to clinicians and trying to decide which would be the best plot to use. Can you decide first whether it is necessary to use a plot at all for clinicians? I find that a diagram—and particularly one with a logarithmic scale—is viewed askance by clinicians, and I wonder what we want to tell them? Do we want to tell them whether the blood is more or less acid than normally, or do we want to tell them the pH, with a little figure in brackets saying normal pH is such and such and this pH is such and such? Then you want to give them some idea as to the two components in the acidæmia or the alkalæmia of the blood, and these two components are surely the P_{CO_2} of the actual blood as taken from the patient and the difference between the bicarbonate value you would have expected for that blood and the bicarbonate that you actually find.

Chairman: People can differ very much in their idea as to how much the biochemist should take the clinician into his confidence, how much he should expect him to understand. Perhaps at one extreme one might have the view that the biochemist tells the clinician: " What you should do for this patient is so and so." At the other extreme we get: " Well, there you have the data. We can express them this way and that way and the other way. Look, you see how they look on this plot. Now I think as a result of this what we should do is so and so." And the view one takes between these two extremes depends very much, I think, on the degree of education of the clinician with whom one is associating.

Severinghaus: I think probably we can garner a little information about how to present this from the way E.K.G.'s are given back to clinicians. They do get back the strip with all the pretty little lines on it, but since they cannot read them the electrocardiographer writes down at the bottom his idea of what a consistent diagnosis is. " This tracing is consistent with left bundle branch block," and I think we can start doing the same. We can send back any kind of a plot we like, but we ought to write at the bottom: " This patient is hypoventilating," because they may not pick that up from the plot.

Wynn: Dr. Astrup's approach is, as I understand it, an attempt at quantitative clinical biochemistry. He presents you not only with a set of figures but he tells you exactly how much acid, or how much alkali, you will have to add to the patient to correct the disorder. If his approach is correct then I for one would want to follow it. My only argument with it is, is it correct for a whole patient? I am sure that in time we will have an answer to that query. Now, as far as presentation of data is concerned, Dr. Nunn has told us that there are six different ways of doing it. To my way of thinking it does not matter how you do it, unless you are going to present the data in a way which can be used quantitatively by the clinician.

IX. THE DETERMINATION OF MIXED VENOUS AND ARTERIAL CO_2 TENSION BY REBREATHING TECHNIQUES

E. J. M. Campbell, Ph.D., B.Sc., M.D., and
J. B. L. Howell, B.Sc., M.B., M.R.C.P.

The Middlesex Hospital, London, W.1.

In this communication we shall be concerned with all those methods which attempt to bring the gas in the lungs into equilibrium with mixed venous blood and to determine the blood P_{CO_2} by analysis of the lung gas. These methods, in effect, all aim to use the lungs as a tonometer, a principle introduced by Plesch (1909) and used extensively for the measurement of mixed venous P_{CO_2} in the course of determination of the cardiac output. These earlier studies have been reviewed by Grollman (1932), Collier (1956) and Defares (1956, 1958). Probably the best known is the breath-holding method of Christiansen, Douglas and Haldane (1914) because, as described in the book by Douglas and Priestley (1948), it is a class experiments in many medical schools.

Five main topics will be discussed. First, an attempt will be made to explain why a method apparently abandoned many years ago for the study of the circulation has recently been introduced into clinical pulmonary physiology. Second, the physiological events underlying the method will be described. Third, the clinical use of the method by Collier and his co-workers will be discussed. Fourth, I will describe studies Dr. J. B. L. Howell and I are at present undertaking to try and extend Collier's results and to simplify the method. Finally a tentative routine method of using the technique will be described.

The Reasons for the Renewed Interest in these Methods

These are both practical and theoretical. The practical reason is the availability of methods for rapid continuous CO_2 analysis which have removed some of the difficulties which troubled earlier workers. The theoretical reason is the realization that the mixed venous P_{CO_2} is predominantly governed by alveolar ventilation and relatively unaffected by changes in cardiac output (Suskind and Rahn, 1954). Thus in a normal subject halving the alveolar ventilation causes the mixed venous P_{CO_2} to rise from 46 to 86 mm.; halving the cardiac output only causes an increase from 46 to 49 mm. A corollary of this conclusion is that the arterio-venous P_{CO_2} difference is small and relatively constant; it changes little with changing cardiac output.

The reason for this relative constancy of the $a - \bar{v}$ P_{CO_2} difference depends upon the fact that any change in cardiac output causes a coincident change in $a - \bar{v}$ O_2 saturation difference and the CO_2 content difference. The change in the O_2 saturation of the mixed venous blood " buffers " the effect of the change in venous CO_2 content on mixed venous P_{CO_2} by the Christiansen-Douglas-Haldane effect.

At this stage it is worth stressing that, although the arterial P_{CO_2} is the best indication of the balance between alveolar ventilation and CO_2 production, it does not necessarily represent the P_{CO_2} of the extracellular fluid. For the purposes of acid-base assessment there is a case to be made for using the mixed venous P_{CO_2}.

There is, furthermore, a practical point in favour of measuring mixed venous P_{CO_2} rather than arterial; it is this. If the arterial blood is withdrawn over too short a period of time, while the subject's ventilation is disturbed by the procedure or some other factor, the arterial P_{CO_2} is liable not to be representative of the steady-state level. The mixed venous P_{CO_2} is much less affected by such temporary disturbances of breathing.

Physiology of the Methods

In general these methods can be divided into two groups: breathholding and rebreathing.

Breathholding Method. (Douglas and Priestley, 1948.) The subject empties his lungs and then inspires a gas mixture of known P_{CO_2}. He holds his breath for a few seconds and then expires about 1 l. (i.e. enough to flush the dead space) and an " alveolar " sample is taken. After a further 6–8 seconds he expires again and a second alveolar sample is collected. If the second sample has a lower P_{CO_2} than the first, the implication is that the initial P_{CO_2} was too high in relation to the mixed venous P_{CO_2}. By repeating this procedure with different CO_2 mixtures the mixed venous P_{CO_2} can be " bracketed ".

This is a good method in trained subjects with normal lungs who can co-operate in the manœuvres. Clinically, however, it is not practicable. The physiological basis of the method is similar in many respects to that of the rebreathing method.

Rebreathing Method. In the method described by Collier (1956) the aim is to have a bag of a CO_2 — air or CO_2 — oxygen mixture which, when rebreathed for a few seconds, mixes with the air in the lungs to give a P_{CO_2} so close to that in the mixed venous blood that complete equilibrium between the bag, the lungs and the venous blood occurs before recirculation causes the mixed venous P_{CO_2} to rise. This equilibrium is recognized by a " plateau " in the record of CO_2 concentration at the mouth as gas passes in and out from the bag to the lungs without changing its CO_2 content (Fig. 2, Curve B).

The mixing of the gas in the bag with that in the lungs and the addition or removal of CO_2 by the pulmonary capillary blood to produce complete equilibrium must in practice occur within about 20 seconds. The processes involved (Fig. 1) will now be considered in more detail.

(1) *Mixing in the Bag.* Complete mixing in the bag probably

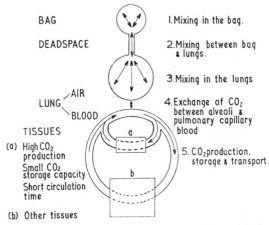

Fig. 1. Processes involved in achieving equilibrium with the mixed venous blood; in limiting the time available; and governing the error introduced if this time is exceeded.

occurs with each breath provided the volume of the bag is not more than twice the tidal volume and it is freely expansile and approximately spherical. We have observed regional variation in concentration in the bag if the tidal volume is small and the expiratory flow rate is slow.

(2) *Mixing Between Bag and Lungs.* This is a dilution process whose rate depends chiefly upon: the frequency of breathing; the size of the tidal volume in relation to the volume of the smaller chamber (i.e. the bag); and the size of the tidal volume in relation to the anatomical and instrumental dead

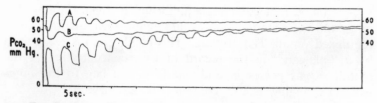

FIG. 2. P_{CO_2} at the mouthpiece during rebreathing.   Records taken from a normal subject at rest rebreathing from a 2 l. bag.   A: initial P_{CO_2} in bag 95 mm. Hg.   B : initial P_{CO_2} 54 mm. Hg. C: initial P_{CO_2} 0 mm. Hg.

Note: (1) The plateau in B extending from 8–13 seconds.   (2) The resemblance of record A to a plateau between 20 and 25 seconds.   (3) The approximation of the P_{CO_2} in B and C at the end of 1 minute.

space.   If the " effective " tidal volume (i.e. the tidal volume minus the dead space volume) is half the bag volume, 90 per cent equilibration will occur in four breaths; if it is a quarter of the bag volume then 90 per cent equilibration will take 8–10 breaths.

This process is therefore partly under control in that as small a bag as possible should be used and the subject can be asked to breathe deeply.   In an unconscious or unco-operative patient or one who has a disease which limits tidal volume, this may not be possible.   As will be discussed later we believe that, in patients with a very small and quiet tidal volume, gas may go in and out of the subject's dead space and a dead space in the neck of the bag changing composition so little as to produce a " bogus plateau " in the record of CO_2 concentration at the mouth.

(3) *Mixing in the Lungs.*   In subjects with normal lungs who

are breathing spontaneously there is almost complete mixing of each tidal volume with the alveolar gas. In other circumstances distribution is much less perfect; for instance, in emphysema there are large parts of the lungs which are under-ventilated and may take many breaths to equilibrate. It is theoretically possible that parts of the lungs with high ventilation: perfusion ratios but which are poorly ventilated in relation to their volume (e.g. cystic areas) could postpone equilibration between the bag and the lungs for many breaths. This does not seem to occur to any significant extent probably because, even in emphysema, ventilation: perfusion ratios are insufficiently disturbed. The evidence that it does not occur is twofold: first, the sloping expiratory CO_2 record of an emphysematous patient becomes flat during the rebreathing procedure; secondly, we have been able to obtain a " plateau " (see above) in all the patients with emphysema we have studied (unless they had severe under-ventilation, which presents a different problem, see later). If maldistribution was sufficiently great, a " plateau " would be unobtainable.

(4) *Exchange of CO_2 Between Alveolar Air and Pulmonary Capillary Blood.* It is important to realize that this is the only process by which the equilibrium can be finally achieved. A subject with a normal CO_2 dissociation curve and a pulmonary capillary blood flow of 70 ml./sec. will take up or give off 0·5 ml. CO_2/sec./mm. Hg tension difference between alveolar gas and mixed venous blood. This being so, the rate at which any difference between the lung-bag P_{CO_2} and the mixed venous P_{CO_2} will decrease depends upon the volume of the lung-bag system. If this be 3 l., any difference in tension will be halved in 5 seconds; if it is 6 l., the difference will be halved in 10 seconds. Thus, if the volume is 3 l., and the initial CO_2 concentration in the bag was so high that the mixture with the lungs was 1 per cent (7 mm. Hg) too high, in 10 seconds the difference between the mixture and the mixed venous blood would be less than 2 mm. Hg.

(5) *The Christiansen-Douglas-Haldane Effect.* The tension of CO_2 with which the alveolar gas comes into equilibrium during rebreathing depends partly upon the oxygen saturation of the pulmonary capillary blood. If the oxygen tension of the alveolar gas at the time of equilibrium is the same as that of the

blood returning to the lungs then the CO_2 tension will not change. If the oxygen tension is higher than that of the mixed venous blood, the equilibrium will be reached with " oxygenated mixed venous blood " and, as pointed out by Christiansen, Douglas and Haldane (1914), this will cause a reduction in the CO_2 capacity of the blood with a consequent rise in CO_2 tension.

The actual rise in CO_2 tension depends upon the magnitude of the change in oxygen saturation, the hæmoglobin concentration and the original CO_2 tension. Complete oxygenation of fully reduced blood of normal hæmoglobin concentration at 40 mm. Hg CO_2 tension would result in an increase in CO_2 tension of 12 mm. Hg; at an initial level of 70 mm. Hg, the rise would be 20 mm. Hg. However, if the blood initially were 30 per cent saturated, the corresponding rises in CO_2 tension with oxygenation would be only 8 and 14 mm. Hg respectively.

We have measured this effect experimentally in two normal subjects (arterial CO_2 tensions of 43 and 38 mm. Hg), in whom we reduced the mixed venous oxygen saturation to 30 and 50 per cent. Oxygenation of this blood during the rebreathing manœuvre increased the CO_2 tension by 6·5 and 4 mm. Hg

TABLE 1. *The Effects of Rebreathing O_2 or 7·5 per cent CO_2 in O_2 for 1–1½ minutes*

Subject	Mixed Venous P_{CO_2} (Collier's Method)	P_{CO_2} in bag after rebreathing 100 per cent O_2		7·5 per cent CO_2
		1 min.	1½ min.	1 min.
1. M . . .	43·0	51·0	52·0	53·0
2. M . . .	48·5	55·5	58·5	57·0
3. M . . .	48·5	47·5	53·5	52·5
4. M . . .	47·5	50·5	54·0	54·0
5. F . . .	45·5	44·0	52·0	50·0
6. F . . .	42·0	45·5	46·0	47·5

Six normal subjects rebreathed either 100 per cent O_2 or 7·5 per cent CO_2 ($\pm$ 0·8 per cent) in O_2 from a 2 l. bag for the times indicated. Note that the P_{CO_2} at the end of the rebreathing period is similar whether the initial P_{CO_2} was 0 or 45–55 mm. Hg.

respectively. We have also calculated from the data of Hackney, Sears and Collier (1958), Table I, Group I, that in 33 subjects in whom the average oxygen saturation of mixed venous blood was presumably about 70 per cent, the average difference between true and oxygenated mixed venous blood was 2·2 mm. Hg. Both of these results are in close agreement with values predicted from the data of Christiansen, Douglas and Haldane (1914).

It is obviously important to determine whether this so-called C-D-H- effect of oxygenation of reduced blood is likely to introduce serious errors into the estimation of mixed venous blood CO_2 tensions for clinical purposes.

The true mixed venous CO_2 tension must lie somewhere between the oxygenated mixed venous and arterial blood CO_2 tensions. In Hackney, Sears and Collier's (1958) series of 60 patients, the maximum CO_2 tension difference observed between oxygenated mixed venous and arterial blood was 11·3 mm. Hg. Because the actual arterial-true mixed venous CO_2 tension difference must have been at least 2–3 mm. Hg, it would appear that in practice, the maximum over-estimation of the CO_2 tension would not be more than 9 mm. Hg. This error would be greatest in patients with severe respiratory acidosis in whom it would not seriously affect the clinical assessment and in whom an overestimate is preferable to an underestimate.

We have now considered the processes concerned in attaining equilibrium with the mixed venous blood. Before considering the other factors—those which limit the time available for obtaining the equilibrium—I would like to point out that, overlapping as they do in time, it should not be unreasonably difficult to attain this equilibrium provided (*a*) the initial CO_2 mixture in the bag is approximately correct—which implies having some estimate of the probable mixed venous Pco_2 within 10 mm. Hg, and (*b*) that the mechanical mixing takes place quickly enough, which chiefly amounts to having an " effective " tidal volume (i.e. tidal − dead space volume) of at least half the bag volume.

The processes which limit the time available for the attainment of the equilibrium and which govern the error introduced if this time is exceeded will now be considered.

(6) CO_2 *Production and Storage in the Tissues and Transport in the Circulation.* The equilibrium mixture will stay unchanged, the air passing in and out of the lungs with no change in CO_2 concentration, until blood which left the lungs unable to give off its CO_2 has passed to the tissues and come back in sufficient volume and with a sufficiently raised P_{CO_2} to increase the mixed venous P_{CO_2}. It is known that some circulations, such as the coronary, have circulation times of only a few seconds. However, empirically both Collier (1956) and ourselves found that an appreciable elevation of the mixed venous P_{CO_2} (as shown by a foothill appearing during expiration in the plateau of the CO_2 concentration at the mouth; Fig. 2 (B)) does not usually occur with the subject at rest until about 20 seconds after the start of rebreathing.

In Fig. 1, the peripheral circulation has been shown in two parts, one going to tissues with a high CO_2 production, small storage capacity and short circulation time and the other going to tissues with lower CO_2 production, large CO_2 storage capacity and longer circulation time. The reason for this representation is to stress that the rate of the initial departure from the plateau value will be dominated by the short circulations while the final rate at which the CO_2 concentration in the whole system (bag—lungs—blood—tissues) will be governed by the rate of CO_2 production and the CO_2 storage capacity of the system as a whole; of these the storage capacity of the tissues is the most important.

We have found in two normal subjects that the rate of rise of CO_2 concentration in the bag in the first 20 seconds after the plateau is 2·7 mm. Hg (range < 0·15 mm. Hg) in 20 seconds and the rate 2½ minutes later is 1·8 mm. Hg (range < 0·1 mm. Hg) in 20 seconds. This second value is almost twice the rate that would be predicted from the studies of Farhi and Rahn (1955) on body gas stores of dogs, possibly because the period we studied is too short for equilibration throughout the whole body CO_2 space. These values were obtained on two normal subjects at rest. As both CO_2 production at rest and CO_2 storage capacity are functions of body size there is no reason to suspect that other subjects who are normal in these respects will differ significantly in the rate at which the CO_2 concentration will rise. Less detailed studies in other normal subjects and in three patients with emphysema are in agreement with this conclusion. It would be expected that subjects with a higher rate of CO_2 production (say due to fever) or reduced storage capacity (due to depleted buffering capacity) may show higher rates. We have so far studied only one such patient, a girl with severe diabetic ketosis and a plasma bicarbonate concentration of 6·3 mEq/l., who in fact only showed a rate of rise in P_{CO_2} of less than 2 mm. Hg in the first 20 seconds after the plateau.

The implication of these data is that failure to obtain complete equilibrium before recirculation occurs will not cause the estimation of mixed venous P_{CO_2} to be seriously in error at least for clinical purposes. Failure to attain equilibrium between the bag, the lungs and the pulmonary capillary blood (i.e. processes 1–4 in Fig. 1) will cause more serious errors.

Accuracy

Before discussing the use of the rebreathing method in practice it is important to decide what degree of accuracy is desirable. This depends on the purpose for which the measurement is to be used.

(1) For the measurement of cardiac output an accuracy of $\pm$ 0·5 mm. Hg is required. This is not attainable by the rebreathing method.

(2) For acid-base studies in which calculation of the pH may be desired an accuracy of $\pm$ 1–2 mm. Hg is desirable when the P_{CO_2} is in the normal range, but $\pm$ 3 mm. Hg would be acceptable when the P_{CO_2} is high (say, over 70 mm. Hg).

(3) For the assessment of the adequacy of alveolar ventilation during anæsthesia or in respiratory disorders an accuracy of $\pm$ 3–4 mm. Hg is perfectly adequate.

In considering these desiderata it is worth remembering that the available methods of blood P_{CO_2} measurement are no more accurate than $\pm$ 2 mm. Hg.

The Use of Rebreathing Methods in Practice

Collier's Method. (Collier, 1956; Hackney, Sears and Collier, 1958; Griggs *et al.*, 1958.)

A small bag is filled with 0·5–1·0 l. of a known CO_2 mixture estimated to be 7–14 mm. Hg above the mixed venous P_{CO_2}.

The subject quietly rebreathes this mixture from the bag for 20 seconds. The concentration of CO_2 is continuously monitored at the mouthpiece with a rapid analyser. The record is examined to see if a " plateau " has been obtained (Fig. 2 B). Collier defines a plateau as " an expiratory CO_2 level, which differs from the preceding inspiratory level by less than 0·1 per cent." If such a plateau is obtained then the P_{CO_2} corresponding to the CO_2 concentration is taken to be mixed venous P_{CO_2}* and the arterial P_{CO_2} to be 6 mm. Hg less.

In a subject whose mixed venous P_{CO_2} is completely unknown the initial bag mixture which is suitable for producing a " good " plateau must be determined by trial and error. It should, however, be noted that starting with a CO_2 mixture which is much too high may produce a record which resembles a " good " plateau (Fig. 2 A).

Hackney et al. (1958) have reported a comparison of the arterial P_{CO_2} as determined in this way and as determined by analysis of the arterial blood in 60 patients and found an average difference of only 0·2 mm. Hg (S.D. 2·9 mm.; maximum error observed 5·3 mm.). However, they do not report results on a further two patients in whom they say the rebreathing plateaux were unsatisfactory. The conditions from which these two patients were suffering are not mentioned. They also include in this paper data to show how much more accurate the rebreathing method is than the end-tidal sample in patients with distribution disturbances.

Griggs et al. (1958) stress how valuable the technique has been in routine clinical use, obviating as it does both the need for arterial puncture and technically difficult analyses, and giving an answer in ten minutes. In a small series of about 20 cases we would agree with these views with the possible exception that we are doubtful if the method is entirely reliable in other than experienced hands when the P_{CO_2} is very high.

Defares' Method. (Defares, 1956; 1958).

This method involves rebreathing 100 per cent O_2 and measuring or recording the rate of rise in CO_2 concentration

---

* This value actually represents the CO_2 tension of " oxygenated mixed venous blood " (page 106). This has been found to be on average approximately 2–3 mm. Hg higher than the true mixed venous CO_2 tension. This increase is included in the 6 mm. Hg subtraction made to obtain the arterial CO_2 tension.

over the first 15–30 seconds. From these data the mixed venous P_{CO_2} is calculated using a formula containing an exponential term. According to Defares' comparison with the Haldane-Priestley breath-holding method the procedure gives very accurate results in normal co-operative subjects. It seems doubtful if the method can be used clinically because of the complexity of the manœuvres involved. Moreover, it is not clear whether or not the mathematical technique is universally applicable.

Personal Studies

Dr. Howell and I are at present investigating the rebreathing method with two main aims. First we hope to simplify the Collier method; and secondly, having simplified it, we want to compare the results obtained with the arterial P_{CO_2} determined by the Riley technique in a range of clinical conditions which might be expected to tax it. I am afraid we have not yet obtained many results because the study is in its early stages. However, I think our findings are already significant and shed light on the rebreathing method in general.

We hope to simplify the Collier method in two ways: first we wish to introduce greater precision in judging the initial CO_2 concentration in the bag and secondly we hope to remove the necessity for a rapid CO_2 analyser.

The way we hope to achieve these aims is by finding a technique of preparing the initial bag CO_2 concentration which is so close to the ideal value that rebreathing it for 20 seconds lowers its concentration to the plateau value. Our approach to this is illustrated in Fig. 2. We observed in ourselves that rebreathing any CO_2-air or CO_2-oxygen mixture from 0 per cent CO_2 up to about 9 per cent CO_2 for 1–$1\frac{1}{2}$ minutes produces a bag concentration $0\cdot5$–$1\cdot5$ per cent (3–10 mm. Hg) above plateau value. The explanation for this follows from the earlier consideration showing that the rate of increase in P_{CO_2} once the mixed venous value has been reached is only about 6 mm. Hg (or less than 1 per cent)/minute. So that, whatever the initial P_{CO_2} in the bag they all approximate to the same rate of change of P_{CO_2} once the excess CO_2 has been absorbed or given off to bring the bags—lungs—blood into equilibrium.

We therefore studied six normal subjects in the following

manner. They " prepared " initial CO_2-air mixtures in three ways: (1) by rebreathing 2 l. of 100 per cent O_2 for 1 minute; (2) by rebreathing 2 l. of 100 per cent O_2 for $1\frac{1}{2}$ minutes; (3) by rebreathing 2 l. of 7·5 per cent CO_2 (53 mm. Hg P_{CO_2}) in O_2 for 1 minute. The CO_2 concentration in the bag was recorded with an infra-red analyser (IRD-O-METER, Infra Red Development Company) checked against a Haldane apparatus.

Table I shows the results together with the mixed venous P_{CO_2} as determined by the Collier method. The second and third methods produced P_{CO_2} values ranging from 4·0–10·0 mm. Hg above the mixed venous blood. Furthermore, rebreathing from bags so prepared produced " good " plateaux in all subjects. The first method produced a CO_2 mixture 4 mm. Hg above mixed venous P_{CO_2} in only two subjects. In these two subjects rebreathing this mixture gave good plateaux. In the other four subjects the P_{CO_2} after 1 minute was less than 4 mm. above the mixed venous value, and rebreathing the mixture gave unsatisfactory plateaux in two of the subjects. Prolonging the period of rebreathing 100 per cent O_2 up to $1\frac{1}{2}$ minutes gave values at least 4 mm. Hg above the mixed venous P_{CO_2}, and rebreathing the gas mixture so prepared produced good plateaux in all subjects.

We also experimented with the preparation of the gas mixture by simply rebreathing expired air for 1 minute. This gave satisfactory results in several subjects, both normal and with various disorders. As will be reported later, patients with obstructive lung disease found this method more unpleasant than the other two—presumably because it made them anoxic whereas the other two methods did not—so we did not study it in detail.

Next we compared the values obtained for the " plateau " with the CO_2 concentration in the bag, after 20 seconds rebreathing. The bag was analysed with a Haldane apparatus. The range of rebreathing periods was 18–27 seconds. In 12 comparisons on six normal subjects the average difference (bag—plateau) was + ·03 mm. Hg P_{CO_2} and the range was + 1·4 to − 0·7 mm. Hg. These values are doubtfully greater than the range of instrumental error.

These results were very encouraging. They suggested two

things: first, that simply rebreathing 100 per cent O_2 for $1\frac{1}{2}$ minutes or 7–8 per cent CO_2 for 1 minute, or even the subject's expired air for 1 minute, would produce a CO_2 mixture just sufficiently higher than the mixed venous P_{CO_2} to be suitable as the starting gas for the Collier method. Secondly they suggested that rebreathing a mixture prepared in any of these ways for 20 seconds and analysing it with a simple chemical analyser would produce results comparable with the Collier method. The next step was to see if the same results could be obtained in a wide range of clinical situations. Theoretical considerations such as those outlined earlier suggested that in clinical practice the following abnormalities might cause difficulty: (i) limitation of ventilatory capacity which by causing dyspnœa might prevent the patient rebreathing long enough to " prepare the bag "; (ii) a small tidal volume or large dead space which might delay the equilibration process and prevent a sufficiently high CO_2 concentration from being attained in the bag in the time available; (iii) a high P_{CO_2} which might prolong the time required to " prepare the bag "; (iv) a high metabolic rate of CO_2 production which might cause the bag prepared by rebreathing to have too high a P_{CO_2}; (v) a reduced body CO_2 storage capacity (due, for example, to depletion of buffering capacity) which might have the same effect; (vi) a high cardiac output which might cause the plateau to be passed in much less than 20 seconds so that analysis of a bag collected after 20 seconds would give an erroneously high result.

A number of these difficulties may, of course, coexist in the same patient and we have not yet accumulated sufficient data to give a final judgment. However our results to date are very suggestive and bear on the rebreathing method in general as well as on our suggested modification of it. The following are our tentative conclusions and the evidence for them.

(1) **High CO_2 Production, Increased Cardiac Output and Reduced Body CO_2 Storage Capacity do not cause the Method to Fail**

Two normal subjects were studied while they were exercising at a rate which caused a CO_2 production in excess of 700 ml./min. (i.e. considerably more than twice their basal rate) and which presumably caused a considerable increase in cardiac output. They prepared bags (while exercising) by rebreathing 100 per cent O_2 for $1\frac{1}{2}$ minutes. Starting with these bags, satisfactory plateaux were obtained at 9–12 seconds in each subject and the P_{CO_2} in the bag after 20 seconds analysed with the Haldane apparatus was only 2 mm. Hg higher than the plateau value.

A patient with an anæmia of 6 Gm/100 ml. and a plasma bicarbonate concentration of 14 mEq./l. due to chronic renal failure was studied by the same technique. Satisfactory plateaux were obtained and the P_{CO_2} of the plateau and of the bag at 20 seconds differed by less than 0·5 mm. Hg.

A patient in severe diabetic ketosis with an arterial pH of 7·12 and a plasma bicarbonate concentration of 6·3 mEq./l. was studied by the same technique. A good plateau was obtained in 10–15 seconds and the record only showed a very slight increase in P_{CO_2} of not more than 2 mm. Hg in the next 20 seconds so that analysis of the bag at 20 seconds would probably have given an estimate of mixed venous P_{CO_2} within 1 mm. Hg of the plateau value. In this patient the arterial P_{CO_2} was also directly determined on two occasions and compared with the " plateau " value. On the first occasion the arterial P_{CO_2} was 16 mm. Hg and the plateau value 19 mm. Hg; on the second the arterial was 23 mm. Hg and the plateau was 26·5 mm. Hg. (Such comparisons are, incidently, likely to be much more reliable than those in patients with severe *under*-ventilation in whom the arterial P_{CO_2} is more labile.)

(2) Reduced Ventilating Capacity and Maldistribution of Inspired Air do not cause the Method to Fail

We have studied three patients with severe obstructive emphysema (all of whom had FEV_1, values of less than 800 ml.) using three techniques of " bag preparation ": (i) rebreathing 100 per cent O_2 for $1\frac{1}{2}$ minutes; (ii) rebreathing 7·5 per cent CO_2 in O_2 for 1 minute; (iii) rebreathing expired air for 1 minute. Satisfactory plateaux and good agreement (i.e. no difference greater than 1·5 mm. Hg) between the P_{CO_2} determined from the plateau and from analysis of the bag after rebreathing for 20 seconds were obtained in all the subjects by both the first and second methods. None of the subjects, however, tolerated the rebreathing of their own expired air very well, presumably because they became anoxic. Less detailed studies of several similar patients using the 100 per cent O_2 for $1\frac{1}{2}$ minutes' technique of bag preparation have given satisfactory results.

(3) Ventilatory Failure may cause both the Collier Method and our Modification to Fail

None of the patients with obstructive disease referred to in (i) above was in severe ventilatory failure. The highest mixed venous P_{CO_2} of the group was 59 mm. Hg.

We have studied two patients with severe ventilatory failure due to obstructive disease. The first, who had an arterial P_{CO_2} of 71 mm. Hg, failed to show a plateau when rebreathing a bag prepared by rebreathing 100 per cent O_2 for $1\frac{1}{2}$ minutes. Satisfactory plateaux were obtained with higher CO_2 mixtures.

The Collier method therefore succeeded but our initial modification failed. In the second patient both the Collier method and our modification failed. This was a patient with very severe emphysema and a funnel deformity of the sternum whom we studied during an acute respiratory infection. His arterial P_{CO_2} was 94 mm. Hg. Neither the rebreathing of 100 per cent O_2 for $1\frac{1}{2}$ minutes nor of 7·5 per cent CO_2 in O_2 for 1 minute prepared bags that gave satisfactory plateaux. He was therefore given bags with initial P_{CO_2} values of 110 and 100 mm. Hg. The first of these gave a plateau of 98 mm. Hg and the second gave an apparently equally good plateau of 91·5 mm. Hg. It appeared that his tidal volume was so small that mixing of the gas in the proximal part of the bag with his dead space produced a " bogus " plateau, the tidal volume being too small in relation to these combined " dead spaces " to introduce gas either from his alveoli or from the main body of the bag to the sampling site in sufficient quantity to change the concentration by more than 0·1 per cent. We have been able to reproduce this effect in ourselves by breathing very shallowly and quietly.

It is difficult to see how the rebreathing method can be made to work with certainty in such an extremely difficult case. At present we believe that the most promising solution is to abandon reliance on the plateau and to use the technique described in the section on " Suggested Routine ".

It is only fair to note in passing that in neither of these two patients would either Collier's method or our modification have been misleading from the clinical standpoint. Indeed, in both cases, the examination of the arterial blood was prompted by the findings with the rebreathing technique.

Suggested Routine

We offer the following suggestions in the confident belief that clinically useful information will be obtained if they are followed. Subsequent experience will be required to assess the accuracy obtainable and will, no doubt, lead to modifications in technique.

(A) If a rapid CO_2 analyser is available and the mixed venous P_{CO_2} is probably within the range 40–50 mm. Hg: fill a bag with $0.5-1$ l. of 8 per cent CO_2 (56 mm. Hg) and have the subject rebreathe it for 20 seconds. If a plateau is obtained there is no need to proceed further.

(B) Whether a rapid CO_2 analyser is available or not, have the subject rebreathe the 2 l. of 100 per cent O_2 for $1\frac{1}{2}$ minutes. Analyse the CO_2 content and empty some of the gas to reduce the volume to about 1 l. After a rest of 3 minutes (the longest rest we have found necessary in normal subjects is 2 minutes) have the subject rebreathe from this bag for 20 seconds.

If the P_{CO_2} of the prepared bag is less than 60 mm. Hg it will probably be found (a) that a satisfactory plateau will be obtained, and/or (b) that the P_{CO_2} in the bag after 20 seconds rebreathing is a few mm. less than that of the prepared bag. Either the P_{CO_2} of the plateau or of the bag after 20 seconds rebreathing will be a satisfactory estimate of the mixed venous P_{CO_2} and can be converted to arterial P_{CO_2} by subtracting 6 mm. Hg.

(C) If the P_{CO_2} in the bag after rebreathing 2 l. 100 per cent O_2 for $1\frac{1}{2}$ minutes is more than 60 mm. Hg; if a satisfactory plateau is not obtained by rebreathing this bag; or if rebreathing this bag for 20 seconds increases its P_{CO_2}:

(1) If a rapid CO_2 analyser is available adopt Collier's trial and error method starting with P_{CO_2} values 10–14 mm. Hg above that found in the bag after rebreathing 100 per cent O_2

for $1\frac{1}{2}$ minutes. Care should be taken to apply stringent criteria before accepting a " plateau ".

(2) If a rapid CO_2 analyser is not available: start again with a bag containing 100 per cent O_2 (reducing its volume if the tidal volume promises to be small enough) and have the subject rebreathe from it for $1\frac{1}{2}$ minutes. After a rest of 3 minutes have the subject rebreathe from this prepared bag for 40 seconds and then analyse it. If the P_{CO_2} in the bag after 40 seconds is less than 4 mm. Hg greater than it was in the bag after 20 seconds during A (above) then the lower (i.e. 20 second) value will probably estimate the mixed venous P_{CO_2} to within $\pm$ 3 mm. Hg.

If the P_{CO_2} in the " 40 second " bag is 6 mm. Hg or more greater than that in the " 20 second " bag the higher value is probably more accurate but may still be an underestimate. A bag with a P_{CO_2} 15–20 mm. higher should then be prepared (this can easily be done by diluting a stock cylinder of, say, 20 per cent CO_2) and rebreathed for periods of 20 seconds and 40 seconds. The P_{CO_2} values in these bags after rebreathing will enable the mixed venous P_{CO_2} to be estimated by interpolation. The accuracy must at present be conjectural, but is unlikely to be worse than $\pm$ 4 mm. Hg. Even this apparently lengthy procedure can be carried out in less than 30 minutes, which still compares favourably with the 45–60 minutes required for arterial puncture and blood gas tension determinations. It is of course also much less demanding in equipment and skill. Moreover, in any individual patient subsequent determinations can be made in much shorter time because the earlier stages can be omitted.

The Use of the Rebreathing Method in Anæsthesia

There would appear to be no serious physiological difficulty about the use of the rebreathing principle in anæsthesia provided the anæsthetic gases do not interfere with the physical or chemical method of analysis which is used. Scurr (1956) has in fact reported a study using the rebreathing technique in conjunction with a Drager CO_2 analyser.

Summary

The relationship between arterial and mixed venous P_{CO_2}, alveolar ventilation and cardiac output are outlined. The physiological basis of rebreathing methods is described. Collier's technique is described and the results obtained with it in clinical practice are reviewed.

Studies are described which were designed to discover ways of simplifying Collier's technique. A routine is outlined which has already been shown to be of clinical value.

Acknowledgements

We wish to thank the Infra Red Development Company Limited for the loan of the " IRD-O-METER " used in these studies.

REFERENCES

CHRISTIANSEN, J., DOUGLAS, C. G., and HALDANE, J. S. (1914). The Absorption and Dissociation of Carbon Dioxide by Human Blood. *J. Physiol.*, **48**, 244.

COLLIER, C. R. (1956). Determination of Mixed Venous CO_2 Tensions by Rebreathing. *J. appl. Physiol.*, **9**, 25.

DEFARES, J. G. (1956). A Study of the Carbon Dioxide Time Course during Rebreathing. *Utrecht*: thesis.

DEFARES, J. G. (1958). Determination of P_{VCO_2} from the Exponential CO_2 Rise during Rebreathing. *J. appl. Physiol.*, **13**, 159.

DOUGLAS, C. G., and PRIESTLEY, J. G. (1948). *Human Physiology.* Oxford: Clarendon Press, pp. 198–207.

FARHI, L. E., and RAHN, H. (1955). Gas Stores of the Body and the Unsteady State. *J. appl. Physiol.*, **7**, 472.

GRIGGS, D. E., HACKNEY, J. D., COLLIER, C. R., and AFFELDT, J. E. (1958). The Rapid Diagnosis of Ventilatory Failure with the Carbon Dioxide Analyzer. *Amer. J. Med.*, **25**, 31.

GROLLMAN A. (1932). *The Cardiac Output of Man in Health and Disease.* London: Baillière, Tindall and Cox, pp. 13–34.

HACKNEY, J. D., SEARS, C. H., and COLLIER, C. R. (1958). Estimation of Arterial CO_2 Tension by Rebreathing Technique. *J. appl. Physiol.*, **12**, 425.

PLESCH, J. (1909). Hämodynamische Studien. *Zeitschr. f. Exp. Path. Therap.*, **6**, 380, pp. 484–499.

SCURR, C. F. (1956). Pulmonary Ventilation and Carbon Dioxide Levels during Anæsthesia. *Brit. J. Anæsth.*, **28**, 422.

SUSKIND, M., and RAHN, H. (1954). Relationship between Cardiac Output and Ventilation and Gas Transport, with Particular Reference to Anæsthesia. *J. appl. Physiol.*, **7**, 59.

DISCUSSION

Chairman: Dr. Campbell has obviously investigated the applicability of this method with patients of various sizes and shapes, and with various affections of their pulmonary system. I would like to ask him how it can be applied to children.

Campbell: Well, I cannot see that there should be any difficulty with children. The diabetic girl was 14 years of age and she was unconscious. I have also done it in a maniacal man and I managed to make it work in him although he was fighting very hard and I would rather have done it to him than try and do an arterial puncture.

Chairman: In children you would use a smaller bag?

Campbell: Oh, I think you would. These are things which, I am afraid, we have not had sufficient experience yet to work out, but maybe if you see the tidal volume is going to be so small by just watching the bag, you just stop, quickly empty some of the gas out and start again. You would not have lost anything. You would be even better off.

Severinghaus: I would like to ask whether there is any reason not to produce hyperventilation either by asking the patient to do it on the bag, or to manually assist a hypoventilating or a comatose patient just to get your equilibration.

Campbell: It won't in any way introduce an error. It will, in fact, help, but we were anxious to work the method out without having to rely on co-operation.

Harbord: How do you get over the difficulty of leakage? Do you put a mask on or do you have a mouthpiece? When I watched you at work last night you seemed to be having difficulty with leakage.

Campbell: No. I have no trouble getting rid of leaks, but last night what I was doing was holding my nose. I should have brought a nose clip with me. With anybody who can use a mouthpiece, we have had no trouble really. With people who have to use a mask we have again really no trouble providing we can just get the mask to fit.

Harbord: That is the difficulty, isn't it?

Campbell: Well, you know that better than I, but we so far have not had very much difficulty.

Harbord: Suppose a patient cannot ventilate into the bag because of a poor apposition between the face and the mask, or has great difficulty in ventilating: I would have thought that you would have met that quite a few times.

Campbell: We have not had to do it so far on patients who have been unconscious and whom we personally have had to ventilate. I should have thought that if you were in that position you would probably use some other method of giving an anæsthetic, in which case you would then have some other method of doing the re-breathing technique.

Wynn: How do anæsthetic gases interfere?

Campbell: This is a problem of the method of gas analysis you use and I am not really qualified to answer that, but I gather that Dr. Nunn has managed to make the Dräger work in the presence of nitrous oxide; and haven't you, Dr. Scurr? I forgot to say that you have used this method.

Scurr: I will try and make one or two comments on this. One is that the use of a mask, by greatly increasing the dead space, will reduce the efficiency of the mixing enormously, because the dead space of the average mask is 150 cc. And the other point I wanted to make was that one meets a number of patients on whom it is desirable to do manual ventilation because of severe bradypnœa and then it is essential to assist the mixing.

Campbell: Well, sir, I do not want to get tangled up with masks, but although the dead space in a mask is 140 cc. a large amount of it is, in fact, poorly ventilated space rather than true dead space. We have not had any trouble in those people in whom we have used masks. The other point was that if you have bradypnœa you may in fact find that you do not get the value high enough in 90 seconds and you may find that you will not get equilibration in 20 seconds. Now, this latter is a problem which is common to the Collier method as well, in which case we suggest that you go to 40 seconds. You may introduce 2 millimetres too much.

Scurr: I have in mind a patient breathing four times a minute, and even if you allow 40 seconds he will only have had about $2\frac{1}{2}$ breaths.

Campbell: Well, you can go on to 60 seconds.

Severinghaus: It would be better to assist the respiration to accelerate mixing of the bag with his lungs?

Campbell: I would be quite happy to do that. I am describing the simple way that we do it. There obviously is no need at all to stick exactly to our routine. What I want to get across are the physiological principles which are involved in any case of this sort of approach, which are that you will get equilibrium within about 40 seconds and the rate at which the CO_2 tension of the system will rise is a function of the time beyond that equilibrium and it is only about 2 millimetres in 20 seconds, and which exact combinations of time you use is a matter for individual design. I cannot take it any further than that at the moment.

Wynn: I take it you accept now that the difference between mixed venous P_{CO_2} and arterial P_{CO_2} is more or less 6 millimetres of mercury as described by Collier, or have you established independently that that is so?

Campbell: We have not established independently that this is so. We have done a small number of comparisons with the arterial. But this introduces another problem which is that it is very difficult to take these measurements simultaneously, because obviously the rebreathing technique disturbs the arterial value and if you do them out of step you may have a time effect introducing a change, and of course in this situation you may be very unfair on any mixed venous method because temporary change of ventilation will have a much more disturbing effect on the arterial value. So it is a little difficult to design a study which specifically settles this, using a rebreathing technique. Of course, if you have a catheter in the pulmonary artery, you could overcome this, but I am not really in a position to do that sort of thing.

Nunn: Do you think that by the end of your $1\frac{1}{2}$ minutes' rest while you are measuring the CO_2, the arterial P_{CO_2} has returned to its original value?

Campbell: I studied this on a number of people and after 1 minute I got a higher value than after 2 minutes' rest. In none of the subjects I have studied has there been any difference between the second and third minute value. The difference between the first and second minute is of the order of 2–3 millimetres.

Nunn: I was interested in the arterial tension. Do you think it would have come back in $1\frac{1}{2}$ minutes' rest?

Campbell: I think it would come back in 30 seconds, probably.

Nunn: If one was comparing arterial tensions directly with the figure given by your technique could one take an arterial sample at that point?

Campbell: No, because it might go through a complicated series of changes. There are lags in the system. Your respiration is being driven by what is happening in the respiratory centre and there will be various time lags to be made up before the whole system is in equilibrium again. You might, in fact, just conceivably have a low P_{CO_2} at a certain stage in the recovery period.

Macrae: Could you apply this method to someone who was being breathed by an artificial respirator?

Campbell: Yes, you just have to have a tap to enable you to turn to a circuit which he could rebreathe from.

Severinghaus: You would disconnect your respirator and connect your patient to a bag?

Campbell: Yes.

Wynn: Ah, but then he stops breathing altogether.

Severinghaus: Then you ventilate with your hands instead of the machine.

Macrae: But does that give you a figure that you could work on?

Campbell: Yes. I think that one of the physiological points about mixed venous blood is that it is so well buffered (to use the word in a loose sense) against temporary change in ventilation that you still get very good clinical guidance, whereas you might not from arterial if there were a period of overventilation while taking the blood.

Chairman: All you need to do, in fact, is to get the air in the patient's lungs exchanging with the bag and it does not matter how you do it.

Campbell: Yes. And what you aim to do is to do it in a sufficiently short period of time not to get too far on in the recirculation, but not so short that you have not got the mixing process complete. And the compromise between these two has to be settled by each individual person. The overestimate introduced by recirculation is not much more than 6 millimetres per minute.

Sykes: Do we know that this 6 millimetres exists in anæsthesia as well as in the conscious patient?

Campbell: Well, we know what the CO_2 production in anæsthesia is, and I do not think the body gas store in anæsthesia changes very much.

Chairman: *Do* we know what the CO_2 production is in anæsthesia? I am beginning to get the impression that perhaps we do not. Or that it may vary very much from one anæsthetic to another.

Nunn: Do you want the CO_2 production, or the output which, after all, governs the difference between venous and arterial tensions? It is the output, I suppose.

Campbell: Well, no. It is not, actually. It is the balance between the two. It is the balance between the CO_2 production and the alveolar ventilation which governs it. Now what is the CO_2 production in anæsthesia? We do not know, you say.

Nunn: The CO_2 output during anæsthesia is generally about 15 per cent below basal.

Campbell: Which would help our method.

Nunn: But can we say what is the production?

Severinghaus: Well, there is no reason to believe that the R.Q. changes greatly. We know the oxygen consumption goes down a little, so CO_2 production probably does too. There are those who try to measure it. I think that is a strange thing to measure as an index of metabolism because it is so dependent upon ventilation and body CO_2 stores.

Wynn: I would not be too happy about accepting the changes described as occurring in anæsthesia, because of any temperature drop, which is quite common, as you were telling us last night. The temperature is often very low.

Severinghaus: Well, in patients we cooled to 30 degrees, the R.Q. reached a steady state between ·75 and ·85 or ·9 depending on the ventilation. I suspect that if you keep a constant ventilation and temperature long enough they would settle back to their original R.Q.

Wynn: It is just a question of time if you go on doing it long enough.

Severinghaus: Temperature is not the prime factor. It is just that if the body temperature drops you may be hyperventilating them.

Campbell: It would have to be an enormous change to shift it far from 6 millimetres per minute. If the CO_2 production dropped to half it would become 3, if you double it, it would rise to 12. If there is a change which doubles it (12 millimetres) we may have to accept the introduction of an overestimate of 4 millimetres in 20 seconds.

Nunn: The cardiac output might change to compensate for that. If the CO_2 production was reduced 15 per cent and the cardiac output was reduced 15 per cent that would preserve the difference, wouldn't it?

Campbell: Well, no. Fifteen per cent reduction in cardiac output would make a negligible difference to mixed venous CO_2 tension. Whereas a 15 per cent reduction in CO_2 production would lower it by about 15 per cent. They cannot cancel each other out because they are working on the process in different ways. One is governing the time which you have available for equilibration and is also governing any value you like to subtract from mixed venous to get arterial. The other factor—that is the rate of CO_2 production—is affecting the rate of build-up throughout the whole system. They work at different points in the system. So although sometimes they could cancel each other out, they are not going to work in such a way that they will inevitably cancel each other out.

Brooks: Would you agree that until we have some method of comparing arterial blood to the values we have for mixed venous P_{CO_2}, we ought to consider this measurement as a new clinical measurement and not really rely on it for comparison with arterial P_{CO_2}? In other words, it is a new clinical factor.

Campbell: I do not think we can legislate here. I think if I measure CO_2 tension by this method clinically I will record the mixed venous CO_2 tension, and if somebody asks me how this compares with the arterial, I will say it will be roughly 6 mm. Hg lower.

Wynn: I think what Dr. Brooks wants to bring out is that Collier failed in two out of 60 cases and you failed in one, I think, of a large number of cases. It does raise a question of what is the failure rate going to be.

Campbell: Well, this failure rate is a relative problem. In both those patients where it failed, they were patients who I already know had CO_2 retention and I went to them to do some more basic study on the time course of these various procedures and from each of them I got values by the very first technique which said to me: "This looks much higher than it was." I then did the further manœuvres and then about half an hour later did an arterial blood. In both cases I was led to do an arterial blood, which showed me these very high CO_2 tensions, by the values I had obtained with the rebreathing method. In neither situation was the value I obtained by this method going to be more than, I think, 8 millimetres wrong. I have to say "I think" because I measured the arterial blood some half an hour later and it might have changed. A small change in alveolar ventilation might have done it. Now,

I am not prepared to say that I have definitely failed with those two patients, because I was 8 millimetres different from an arterial CO_2 tension measured, maybe, half an hour later.

Severinghaus: No. The word " fail " probably is not applicable here. It just means that your error is slightly greater. Ten millimetres in a hundred is not very much.

Campbell: The failure really comes from the fact that I did not by this first procedure get a good plateau in the Collier sense. That is what I really mean by failure. If you take the value I obtained and compare it with what the patient's P_{CO_2} probably was, we will not say failure, we will say I had an error which might have been as great as 8 millimetres Hg; and in a patient with a P_{CO_2} of 94 that was not going to lead to clinical harm.

Wynn: It is interesting that you should raise that point about it not being a failure because it was 10 millimetres away from the true value. If we are going to accept that sort of limit of error why not just use the end-tidal sample?

Severinghaus: And what is your error? Thirty millimetres easily.

Wynn: Thirty? In an end-tidal sample?

Severinghaus: Yes.

Wynn: In an emphysematous patient?

Severinghaus: Or even in one without emphysema, with a pulmonary embolism, for example. Or hyperventilation.

Campbell: Examination of Fig. 3 (reproduced from Hackney, Sears and Collier's (1958) paper which I referred to this morning would settle the point. The other thing is that you have to have a machine that will take an end-tidal sample. With this method you just to have to have a bag. For an end-tidal measurement you have either to have a very rapid analyser, or you have got to have one of these very tricky little Otis-Rahn gadgets which are difficult to keep going. And house physicians in city hospitals are not going to mess about with those.

Severinghaus: I also did not mean that I would not settle for 10 in 40. I said 10 in a 100.

Macrae: We found that the end-tidal sample was not very reliable.

Wynn: In what sort of patients?

Macrae: People on artificial respiration.

Wynn: Polio patients?

Macrae: Yes. If the lungs are normal it gives a good answer. If the lungs are in any way abnormal it does not give a good answer, and of course the abnormal ones are the ones we wanted to spot.

Severinghaus: Well, according to our thesis the end-tidal is better for telling you how bad the pulmonary circulation is than how bad the ventilation is.

Macrae: Yes. That is true.

Harbord: What sort of errors do you get from the absorption of CO_2 into the water of the bag in that time?

Campbell: None in the time. The analysis is done within 20 seconds, you see.

Macrae: But you do get a loss if the sample remains in the rubber bag for a long time.

Campbell: Yes, but I do not hang on to it for a long time.

Brooks: How are you going to avoid the difficulty of maldistribution in patients with pathological conditions of the lungs?

Campbell: Well it does not enter into the rebreathing method, because maldistribution, which completely wrecks the end-tidal,

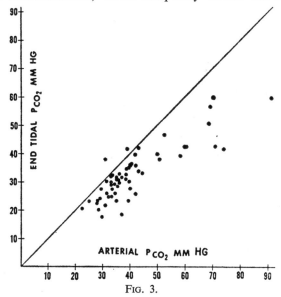

FIG. 3.

just slightly delays the time for equilibration. You see, people worry. They say: " Look at the enormous residual capacity and dead space " and so on, if there is emphysema. This is because people have been making the wrong measurement in emphysema for so long. In fact, the alveolar dead space in emphysema is rarely more than 30 per cent of the tidal volume. This means that within about three breaths or so you have brought your alveolar dead space into equilibrium with the system. There is no large mass of gas in the lungs that is being under-ventilated sufficiently to cause a problem.

Severinghaus: That, too, though is not going to affect the problem at all. If you have areas of the lung which are not being perfused the gas within them will also come to equilibrium, provided it is being ventilated, with the gas in the bag and the rest of the lung. In fact, I do not think there is any known pathology of the lung which would defeat this equilibrium.

Third Session

X. RECENT DEVELOPMENTS IN BLOOD O_2 AND CO_2 ELECTRODES

J. W. Severinghaus, M.D.

Cardiovascular Research Institute and Department of Anesthesiology, University of California Medical School

I WOULD like to describe the present status of the oxygen and carbon dioxide electrodes as I have been using them for the direct determination of these gas tensions in liquid, particularly blood. Accurate blood gas tension measurement has been one of physiology's most trying pursuits. The determination of oxygen tension has depended on various methods, none of

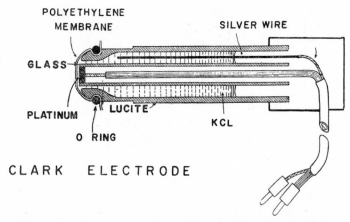

FIG. 1. The polarographic oxygen electrode.

which were accurate at high oxygen tensions. Accurate blood carbon dioxide tension on single samples has been possible by the indirect computation of pH and plasma CO_2 content, on equilibration with gas bubbles or on tonometry of a sample of blood at several known CO_2 tensions, followed by pH measurement. There have been no rapid methods for continuous determination of either gas until the introduction of polarography.

The oxygen electrode which I have incorporated in the apparatus to be described was designed by Dr. Leland C. Clark (1956) of the Fels Research Institute. His unique contribution was the separation of the entire electrical cell from the blood by a polyethylene membrane which is permeable to oxygen (and CO_2) but not to electrolytes and solutes which had poisoned bare platinum electrodes (Fig. 1). He used a platinum disc 2 mm. in diameter sealed into the end of a glass tubing as the cathode, charged to -0.5 to -0.6 volts. At the platinum surface, dissolved oxygen molecules react by receiving electrons and becoming either OH^- or H_2O_2. The current which may be passed from this platinum surface is linearly related to the availability of dissolved oxygen gas molecules at its surface. In this electrode, this is directly proportional to the partial pressure of oxygen at the polyethylene surface. Without oxygen there is virtually no current. The current leaves the solution through a silver-silver chloride reference electrode in the surrounding reservoir of saturated KCl.

To determine blood oxygen tension accurately with the Clark electrode, the following criteria must be met: (1) temperature constant to $\pm 0.1°C.$; (2) no pressure change in the liquid; (3) ability to calibrate with known gas tensions in the same liquid (e.g. blood) stirred at the same rate; (4) an anaerobic environment which can neither contribute nor remove oxygen from the blood (i.e. no trapped bubbles and the walls of the chamber must not oxidize, absorb or dissolve oxygen); (5) stirring of the liquid at the surface at constant velocity.

The most serious problem with this electrode is that it uses up the oxygen from the environment surrounding the polyethylene surface. In gas this is not a problem because of the rapid diffusion of gas molecules. But in liquids, particularly blood, rapid stirring is required to keep the oxygen tension constant at the membrane surface. If this oxygen is not rapidly replaced either by diffusion or by mixing, the observed current falls off with time to almost zero. This problem can be reduced by (1) rapid stirring; (2) thicker or less permeable membranes; (3) smaller diameter cathodes. One electrode made by Beckman Instrument Company to pass through an 18-gauge intravenous needle, has a $0.001''$ cathode and is said to have almost no need for stirring. It therefore has a much weaker current available for measurement. If either thicker or less permeable membranes are used, a greater time lag is introduced and the current is reduced. In highly viscous solutions such as blood (2–5 centipoises), the error will be unacceptable unless constant rapid stirring allows calibration to be done with the same blood equilibrated with known tensions. We have tried four different stirring methods, each of which has disadvantages. Because of the importance of this part of the design, these will be described in some detail.

Methods of Stirring

A. By flowing the blood: the rate of flow is critical. Much depends on having the jet stream impinge on the electrode membrane to keep replacing the blood at the surface. Turbulence is by nature erratic and the flow pattern in the cuvette may change from time to time. The calibrating blood sample must be made to flow at exactly the same rate and pattern and at the same pressure at the electrode surface, which is extremely difficult if viscosity changes with oxygen saturation, as it seems to. Large volumes of blood are needed for calibration. Temperature must be exactly the same in the calibrating blood as in the unknown blood. The entire calibrating sample must have constant Po_2. Ways have been devised by others, interested in measuring Po_2 in flowing blood, to circumvent most of these problems, but the mechanical engineering difficulties are considerable.

B. Pulsing the blood back and forth: a device was built to compress and release a $\frac{1}{8}''$ rubber tube leading into the chamber at variable rates to force blood back and forth across the membrane surface. This was unsatisfactory because stirring did not appear to be uniform, because the blood moving in and out exchanged oxygen with the rubber tubing and the distal end of the line and because pressure changes were unavoidable at the membrane surface. Avoiding these difficulties appeared to make this method too complicated.

C. Magnetic stirring bobbin in the cuvette: this method was tried and has the advantage that no stirring shaft need enter the chamber. It failed because (*a*) the position of the bobbin was variable; (*b*) its rate of spin was less in more viscous bloods; (*c*) it was difficult to design a bobbin which stirred vigorously near the electrode surface but never jumped up and damaged the membrane.

D. Stirring paddle on a shaft: there were a number of less successful attempts with this most obvious method. The present design (Fig. 2) utilizes a tiny paddle and stainless steel

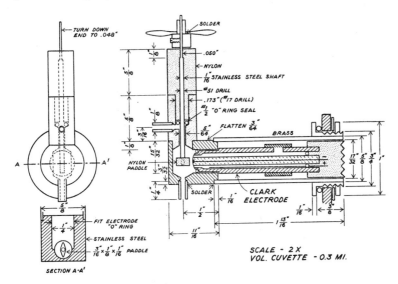

CUVETTE FOR OXYGEN ELECTRODE

FIG. 2. The cuvette showing method of sealing a stirring paddle and shaft into the analysis chamber.

shaft sealed in the top of the cuvette by an " O " ring. The paddle edge should sweep within $\frac{1}{16}$" of the electrode face and this distance must not change during use since the calibration in blood depends upon it.

Cuvette Design

Lucite chambers of various shapes have been made. Unfortunately, the solubility of oxygen in lucite seems to be enough to give hysteresis effects as bloods of differing oxygen tension are put in the chamber. That is, oxygen either dissolves into or out of the walls depending on whether the previous oxygen tension was lower or higher than the new one. Furthermore, lucite conducts heat very poorly, delaying thermal equilibrium. Brass and nickel plating were used for several chambers, but something caused rapid falls in the observed oxygen tension and corrosion was apparent.

The present chamber (Fig. 2) is of stainless steel and is satisfactory, having no measurable hysteresis or oxygen utilization. The interior surfaces are polished. Metal can be made with walls thinner than plastic or glass and conducts heat much better, but lacks the advantage of transparency (to see bubbles). The present design has no horizontal surfaces to trap air bubbles. The design is such that the " O " ring on the electrode is positioned at the innermost end of its housing, leaving no horizontal lip. The bubble problem is one of the chief reasons for mounting the electrode horizontally. This permits blood to fill the chamber from bottom to top smoothly, carrying out the surface layer which has been exposed to air.

Water Bath

A small water bath was constructed to house the electrodes, together with a tonometer for preparing blood samples of known oxygen tension for calibration of the oxygen electrode. A three-way stopcock was mounted inside the bath so that the electrode could be directly filled either with unknown sample from a syringe outside the bath or with calibrating blood flowing from the tonometer through a connecting tube inside the bath. This eliminated the need for a syringe transfer of calibrating blood to the electrode. The bath also contains a stirring paddle, heater, thermostat, humidifier for the gas entering the tonometer, Luer fittings for inlet and outlet of both electrodes and a thermometer. The bath and the oxygen electrode cuvette are stirred with a 2400 rpm. shaded pole induction motor. The tonometer drum, mounted eccentrically, is rotated at 60 rpm. by a synchronous clock motor. In the commercial production model* (Fig. 3) the thermostat is replaced by a thermistor electronic temperature controller.

* Yellow Springs Instrument Company, Yellow Springs, Ohio.

FIG. 3. The left face of the water bath has the CO_2 electrode and its inlet and outlet, and the control knob for a three-way stopcock on the oxygen electrode cuvette. The right face has the oxygen electrode, its inlet and outlet, the inlet for gases used in the tonometer, the plug closing the tonometer, and a drain plug.

To face p. 130.

Oxygen Electrode Current Measurement

To obtain accuracy to 0·1 per cent of full scale, a null balance meter was designed. It employs a two-transistor amplifier, a fifty-microampere meter as balance indicator and a ten-turn linear potentiometer with a microdial. The electrode current is exactly opposed by adjustment of this potentiometer. The span of the dial may be adjusted to make it read directly in P_{O_2}, percentage oxygen or 0–1000. The Clark electrode has a small current in the complete absence of oxygen, usually less than the equivalent of 1 per cent oxygen. This residual current may be bucked out with a screwdriver control, so the microdial reads zero when P_{O_2} is zero. A new feature is a push-button to test for leaks in the electrode membrane by applying a voltage between the reference silver electrode and the cuvette body. Leak is indicated by deflection of the balance indicator meter. There are outlet jacks for an external recorder, such as a galvanometer or self-balancing potentiometer. In this case, zero may be suppressed with the microdial to make the recorder span a narrow range such as 500 to 700 mm. Hg. The circuit diagram of the device has been published elsewhere (Severinghaus and Bradley, 1958).

Washing Solution

The solution used to rinse the cuvette between analyses has two functions beyond that of cleansing. It must prevent bubbles of air from clinging to the cuvette walls during filling with sample and it must help drain the membrane surface free of droplets for gas calibration, particularly in the oxygen electrode where a tiny droplet on the membrane over the platinum will reduce inward diffusion of oxygen. The following solution is kept at 38°.

General Electric Silicone Antifoam 60   0·1 ml.
Alconox (hæmolysing detergent)   .   0·1 g.
Water   .   .   .   .   .   .   1000 ml.

Methods of Filling the Cuvette

The concern about anaerobic handling of the blood led us to try mercury displacement. This was abandoned because (*a*) it attacks hard and soft solder joints and the stopcock; (*b*) it picks up various oxidizable substances and tends to leave them on the cuvette walls, leading to rapid falls in O_2 tension; (*c*) it breaks up into a blood-mercury emulsion which will not separate; (*d*) it requires an external levelling system, which adds additional problems in thermal regulation of the mercury.

If the chamber is filled slowly from below while the stirrer is stationary, a 2 ml. sample is sufficient to wash through the cuvette to a stable P_{O_2}. The stirrer should be turned on after blood appears at the outflow tubing to dislodge any bubbles which may have adhered to the walls. All solutions should be at electrode temperature when introduced.

To drain the cuvette for gas calibration, we wash it with the detergent antifoam solution, turn off the stirring paddle and drain it slowly. We find it best to set the stirring paddle parallel to the electrode membrane to prevent a droplet of water from clinging between the edge of the paddle and the membrane. This is easily done if the bath propeller is in line with the stirring paddle on the shaft. If gas calibration is done with the stirrer turning, droplets of water may be thrown on to the membrane, decreasing the reading.

Calibration

The zero oxygen point may be calibrated either with an oxygen absorbing solution, such as is used in gas analysis apparatus, diluted about 100 times with water, or with an oxygen free gas. The absorbing solution must be rinsed out with an acid bichromate solution. If tank nitrogen is used, its oxygen content should be analysed, it being usually 0·2 per cent.

It is most convenient to set the amplifier sensitivity against a gas of known P_{O_2}, such as air or oxygen, since this value can be repeatedly checked and reset in case the electrode drifts. The cuvette interior must be wet and gas flow through it must be stopped to achieve water vapour saturation at 37° C. The electrode often drifts upward, so it is well to calibrate at less than full scale at the outset.

Five or more ml. of the unknown, prewarmed blood are put into the tonometer and equilibrated with the calibrating gas for about 15 minutes. The gas is humidified in the lucite bubbler tube inside the water bath and flowed through the tonometer at about 20–100 ml./min. This equilibrated blood is pulled directly from the tonometer through the inside three-way stopcock into the cuvette, and its reading divided into that of the gas. The readings on the blood samples are multiplied by this ratio.

Response of the O_2 Electrode

Table I demonstrates the response of the Clark electrode as affected by various membranes, the diameter of the platinum and the rate of stirring. The high current obtained with teflon is offset by two disadvantages: the stirring error is greater and the utilization of oxygen from the sample in the cuvette is greater. For example, with a 0·3 ml. cuvette, it was computed, and observed, that 1·5 per cent of the oxygen dissolved in water in the cuvette is used per minute by the 2 mm. platinum electrode covered with 0·001″ teflon membrane.

TABLE I. *Comparison of various membranes used with the oxygen electrode. P_{O_2} — 713 mm. Hg gas reading set to 100. Platinum diameter 2 mm. 37° C. Liquid test solution viscosity: 5 centipoises (glycerol 58 per cent in water). Figures in parenthesis were obtained with an electrode having a platinum diameter of 1 mm.*

		Teflon 0·001″	Polyethylene 0·001″	Mylar 0·00025″
Background current for zero P_{O_2} (μ amp.) . . .		·004–·02	·01–·02	·006–·01
Current with gas of P_{O_2} 713 mm. Hg. (μ amp.) . .		32	7	·09
Response time to 99 per cent (sec.)		20	40	120
Reading in liquid of P_{O_2} 713 mm. Hg.				
Stirring rate	0 rpm.	—	—	78–90
	60 rpm.	—	—	96–97
	800 rpm.	70(79)	89(90)	99–100
	2400 rpm.	81(86)	93(93)	99–100

Polyethylene is, therefore, a better membrane provided the lower current can be determined accurately.

Blood appears to use oxygen at rates up to 1 ml./litre/min. while being rapidly stirred; whereas when it is stationary in a syringe, the rate is usually about 0·1 ml./litre/min. This was found to be largely a result of white blood cell metabolism. This results in P_{O_2} falling as much as 4 per cent per minute at high tensions.

The observed current tension for any given gas tends to drift upward more rapidly at high oxygen tensions. The cause of this drift is probably the accumulation of H_2O_2, shifting the reaction to produce more OH^-. Sometimes crystals appear to grow at the edge of the platinum and change the zero oxygen current. This is reduced by using less than saturated KCl solution.

The CO_2 Electrode

In 1955 Stow (Stow, Baer and Randall, 1957) first described a CO_2 electrode in which a latex membrane separated the sample to be measured from a film of distilled water on the surface of a glass electrode. The CO_2 in the blood diffused through the rubber into the water, until P_{CO_2} equilibrium occurred. The pH of the water film was found to be related to log P_{CO_2}. Drift and insensitivity were such that the electrode was not dependable.

It can be shown theoretically that the sensitivity of such an electrode is doubled if, instead of distilled water, a dilute solution of bicarbonate is used against the glass electrode. Paradoxically, (sodium) bicarbonate is not a buffer for CO_2, which is one of its constituents. The basic equation, derived from the mass and electroneutrality laws, is:

$$\alpha P_{CO_2} = H_2CO_3 = \frac{{}^aH^2 + {}^aH{}^aNa - K_w}{\left(K_1 \left(1 + \dfrac{2 K_2}{{}^aH} \right) \right)}$$

where α is the solubility of CO_2, K_w the dissociation constant of water, a the activity of hydrogen and sodium, and K_1 and K_2 the first and second dissociation constants of H_2CO_3 (to bicarbonate and carbonate). From this it may be computed that in distilled water the relationship between pH and P_{CO_2} is:

$$S = \frac{\Delta\ pH}{\Delta \log P_{CO_2}} = 0.5 \text{ (Defining " S " as sensitivity of the electrode)}$$

whereas in bicarbonate solutions between 0·001 M and 0·01 M,

$$S = \frac{\Delta\ pH}{\Delta \log P_{CO_2}} = 1.0$$

This suggests that the inclusion of bicarbonate ion in the aqueous medium should double the sensitivity of the electrode. This was found to be true in samples of varying HCO_3 con-

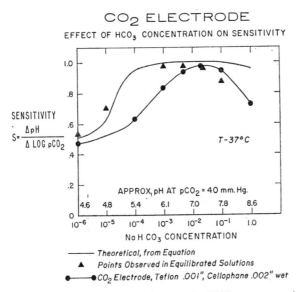

FIG. 4. The relationship of pH to pCO_2 at varying HCO_3^- concentrations, showing general agreement between theory and tonometer equilibrated solutions. The decreased sensitivity observed in the CO_2 electrode with dilute solutions may be due to buffer groups in cellophane.

centrations prepared in a tonometer. These theoretical and observed sensitivity curves have been plotted in Fig. 4. At higher concentrations, sensitivity falls off again as the carbonate ion appears. At 1·0 M $NaHCO_3$, S = 0·88 according to equation (1), but this is an approximation due to the changes in activity in high concentrations. It was noted that equilibration time in a tonometer was greatly prolonged in solutions above 0·02 M, requiring about 15 minutes at 0·1 M and more than two hours at 1 M, as compared with about five minutes for all more dilute solutions. The reasons for this delay and fall in sensitivity probably stem from the fact that more CO_2 must be exchanged as increasing amounts of carbonate occur. The pH values were taken from the water and bicarbonate solutions equilibrated with 6·06 per cent CO_2 and are in reasonable agreement with the calculated values.

On the basis of this theory and the confirmatory experiments, a dilute sodium bicarbonate solution was used to make the CO_2 electrode. The sensitivity was still not as great as predicted and drifting was severe. Further analysis of the problems suggested two modifications.

First, it was suspected that the aqueous film held on the surface of the glass electrode was too thin to be adequately conductive, so that the electrode was partly non-functional. In order to provide a uniform space between glass and membrane, a cellophane dialysing membrane was soaked in the bicarbonate and interposed between them. This brought the sensitivity up to about 0·95 (using 0·005 to 0·01 M bicarbonate).

It became apparent that the drift was primarily occurring at the silver reference electrode as the silver chloride plating dissolved in the bicarbonate solution. At the suggestion of Dr. Roger Bates of the National Bureau of Standards, we added 0·1 M NaCl to the electrolyte to depress silver solubility maximally. In addition, the electrolyte was saturated with silver chloride by adding a drop of 0·1 M $AgNO_3$ per 100 ml. of electrolyte. This has completely eliminated the drift. The cellophane is soaked in this solution for several hours before assembly.

Cast teflon film* has been the most satisfactory membrane material.

The most recent design† of the CO_2 electrode is shown in Figs. 5 and 6. A special glass electrode,‡ designed for this purpose, has the following characteristics: (*a*) a relatively

---

* Dilectrix Corporation, Grant Avenue, Farmingdale, L.I., N.Y.
† National Welding Company, 218 Fremont Street, San Francisco, Calif.
‡ Beckman Instrument Company, 2500 Fullerton Road, Fullerton, Calif.

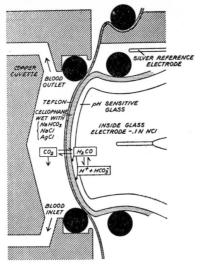

FIG. 5. Schematic design of CO_2 electrode. The function of the cellophane film is to hold a uniform thin layer of electrolyte at the glass membrane surface to ensure adequate conductivity edgewise and to overcome the buffering effect of the glass itself.

flat sensitive glass membrane to permit flat teflon and cellophane films to be tightly applied without wrinkles; (*b*) an enlarged side wall to accommodate the air bubble within the

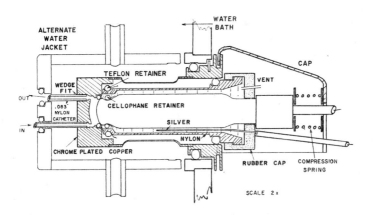

CO₂ ELECTRODE

FIG. 6. The special glass electrode and associated cuvette assembly for determination of pCO_2 in liquid or gas.

electrode and permit horizontal mounting; (c) a neck narrowed
to hold an " O " ring which is used to mount the cellophane
on the electrode; (d) a 60″ lead.

The cuvette cannot be lucite (perspex) because of CO_2
solubility and thermal lag. Brass reacts with some solutions.
Stainless steel is good, but for best thermal equilibration,
chrome-plated copper has been chosen. The sample is introduced through a nylon catheter wedged into the cuvette. The
seal between the membranes and the cuvette is made with an
" O " ring. The electrolyte jacket is machined from nylon
rod and a latex rubber cap closes the outer end and holds the
reference electrode.

The electrode is capable of being thermostatically controlled
in three ways. It may be mounted in the side of a water bath,
such as the bath of the oxygen electrode. The instrument
being made by Yellow Springs Instrument Company has an
orifice designed for mounting this CO_2 electrode. Or it may
be mounted with one of two jackets made by its manufacturer,
one a waterjacket going over the electrode to permit thermostatically controlled water to be circulated by a pump around
it, the other an air jacket over the opposite end to permit the
electrode to be immersed in whatever water bath is available.

Assembly

The latex cap is mounted on the glass electrode and a
chlorided silver wire mounted through it. This electrode is
16–18 gauge sterling silver wire, given a chloride coat by
plating in 0.1 N HCl at 10–20 milliamperes for about a half-
hour. The thinnest available dialysing membrane cellophane
($.0008″$) is soaked in electrolyte for several hours. It is stretched
over the glass electrode and held in place with an " O " ring.
Teflon film ($0.001″$ for general purpose, $0.00025″$ for fastest
response) is mounted on the nylon electrolyte chamber using
silicone stopcock grease to make a tight seal (important for
electrical insulation). The nylon tube is partly filled with
electrolyte. The glass electrode, electrolyte jacket and cuvette
are assembled as shown and held together with a compression
spring and retainer cap. Electrolyte should fill the nylon
chamber completely for good thermal equilibrium.

Response of the CO₂ Electrode

A. Linearity: The relationship of pH to log P_{CO_2} is linear within 0·002 pH from 1 to 100 per cent CO_2 concentration in calibrating gas, or from 7 to 700 mm. Hg (Fig. 7). From

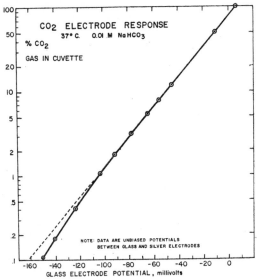

Fig. 7. Linear relationship of Δ log pCO_2 to E.M.F. or pH.

1 per cent down to 0·1 per cent the response is very slow and appears to become non-linear, but can be calibrated and used. Δ pH/Δ log P_{CO_2} is slightly less than 1·0, probably due to a variety of factors, such as edge sensitivity in areas not equilibrated with the gas, electrical leakage in the leads, buffering of the cellophane, and buffering of the small amount of carbonate ion present. These factors, however, appear to be surprisingly constant and the sensitivity has uniformly been 0·95 ± 0·02. With one particular electrode and pH meter the variation is less than 0·003 from week to week. This means that a calibration curve can be permanently prepared.

Speed of Response

The response is complete in thirty seconds at 100 per cent CO_2 with 0·001″ teflon membrane. However, when going to

3 per cent CO_2, 99 per cent response is completed in about two minutes, and to 0.1 per cent CO_2 it may exceed ten minutes. With $0.00025''$ teflon, the rate is about twice as fast. When thinner cellophane becomes available it may be made faster by having a lesser water film*. We have been unsuccessful in trying to accelerate the response with carbonic anhydrase. Polyethylene, silicone rubber and latex rubber membranes are slower than teflon and the latter two tend to become water-logged and very slow.

If the electrolyte bicarbonate concentration is increased the response becomes very much slower, requiring about one-half hour with 1 M $NaHCO_3$. Dilute solutions respond considerably faster, but the sensitivity decreases.

Method of Calibration

As was anticipated, the response of the CO_2 electrode to blood and gas of the same P_{CO_2} is identical. This happy situation makes possible calibration of the instrument with accurately analysed compressed gases and no blood need be equilibrated. In practice, a gas of about 6 per cent CO_2 is used as a standard to set the meter zero and the response to 100 per cent CO_2 is checked for slope. Although one might think greater accuracy would be obtained by using a bracketing gas, such as 4 per cent or 8 per cent, the 100 per cent has several advantages. Response is very fast, the gas need never be analysed and the spread on the instrument permits more accurate reading of the slope of the response.

Washing and Filling the Cuvette

The electrode must be mounted horizontally because it permits samples to be inserted in the bottom catheter, displacing all the air from the chamber; and it permits gas to be introduced from the top displacing all liquid out of the bottom. After sampling, the same detergent antifoam solution used in the oxygen electrode is used to wash out blood. The electrode should be filled with a gas having a P_{CO_2} similar to that of the sample before introducing samples to minimize the effect of exposure of the surface film and to speed the equilibrium.

* Available in W. Germany as " Cuprophane " from the J. P. Bemberg Co., Wuppertal.

Drift

There are two causes of drift in the potential of the electrode. The membrane may have a hole, or the reference electrode may need a new AgCl coating. The presence of a hole can be detected electrically with an ohmeter between the silver reference electrode and the cuvette body where no conductivity (infinite resistance) should be found (with the cuvette filled with sample, saline or any conducting liquid). The reference electrode needs recoating, if jiggling it in the rubber cap causes change in the potential of the P_{CO_2} electrode.

Indicating and Recording Instruments

The relatively small changes in pH occurring in the electrode require a pH meter with an expanded scale. 0·01 pH change is the equivalent of 2·5 per cent change in P_{CO_2}, or 1 mm. Hg in 40 mm. Hg. It is desirable to read to 0·001 pH (60 microvolts) to obtain accuracy approaching 0·1 mm. Hg. Standard potentiometers may be used with a null balance electrometer indicator. A vibrating reed electrometer with unity gain may be connected to standard millivolt self-balancing recorders, or to any high gain d.c. amplifier and pen recorder. The input impedance of the electrometer should be above 10^{12} ohms for recording, 10^{10} ohms if null balance is used.

Continuous Flow Measurements

Heparinized blood has been perfused continuously from dogs' arteries and veins through the electrode, returning it to the animal. The metal parts should be coated with silicone to decrease fibrin formation. The metal, nylon and teflon materials may be autoclaved, and the rubber " O " rings boiled briefly if sterilization is desired. We have not yet used it in this way with patients.

Tissue Surface P_{CO_2}

Preliminary experiments indicate that it is possible to calibrate the electrode in the cuvette, and then remove the glass electrode with the nylon jacket and membranes intact, and press the electrode against tissue to obtain some information about tissue P_{CO_2}. The effect of carbonic anhydrase inhibition on brain P_{CO_2} is being investigated in this way. It is necessary to make a circulating water jacket to control electrode temperature.

Summary

A Clark polarographic oxygen electrode and a new design of CO_2 electrode have been built into cuvettes in a 1 litre 37° water bath, together with a tonometer for preparing blood of known oxygen tensions. The oxygen cuvette holds 0·3 ml. of blood, is stirred by a paddle on a driven shaft and may be filled with blood from the tonometer using a three-way stopcock mounted within the bath. Sample viscosity reduces the response sufficiently that stirring at constant rate is required. Polyethylene appears better than teflon, having less viscosity error due to its five-fold reduction in current. A null balance accurate current meter is used to read P_{O_2} or per cent O_2 directly on a dial.

The CO_2 electrode is a glass pH electrode separated from the sample of unknown P_{CO_2} by a teflon membrane and a cellophane film wet with dilute bicarbonate into which the CO_2 diffuses from the sample. The sample P_{CO_2} determines the pH in the aqueous cellophane. The CO_2 cuvette holds 0·2 ml. of blood and may be calibrated with gas, the response being linear (on semi-log paper) from 1 per cent to 100 per cent CO_2. Sensitivity is such that 0·01 pH change is a 2·5 per cent change in P_{CO_2}. Response time is about one to two minutes. Response is independent of flow, pressure or viscosity. Drift has been virtually eliminated.

REFERENCES

CLARK, L. C., Jr. (1956). Monitor and Control of Blood and Tissue Oxygen Tensions. *Trans. Amer. Soc. Art. Int. Organs*, **2,** 41.
SEVERINGHAUS, J. W., and BRADLEY, A. FREEMAN (1958). Electrodes for Blood P_{O_2} and P_{CO_2} Determination. *J. appl. Physiol.*, **13,** 515.
STOW, R. W., BAER, R. F., and RANDALL, B. F. (1957). Rapid Measurement of the Tension of Carbon Dioxide in Blood. *Arch. phys. Med.*, **38,** 646.

DISCUSSION

Chairman: Dr. Severinghaus, how close are you to what I suppose would be our ideal, continuous measure of tensions of oxygen and CO_2 in blood?

Severinghaus: We have used the CO_2 electrode in the dog, per-fusing the blood through it continuously. Of course you need to heparinize the animal. The response time of the CO_2 electrode is increased in proportion to distance over which it has to travel, and inversely proportional to the P_{CO_2}. Using the new flatter electrode we have been able to use thinner teflon—down to $0.00025''$, and $0.005''$ cellophane—giving complete response in 30 seconds. With the oxygen electrode I have not yet tried continuous measure-ments although many people do it in the heart-lung machine. I think they are not interested in such accuracy with that as we are looking for in biological measurements. They want to avoid supersaturating the blood with oxygen for which purpose I think this is a very nice technique. You could put it in without the elaborate stirring precautions which are necessary if you want accurate measurements and get a continuous reading. Both of these things can very easily be made to read out continuously on recorders.

Chairman: Dr. Nunn, would you like to open the discussion on that?

Nunn: I am intrigued that the maximum sensitivity should be a slope with $\Delta pH/\Delta log\ P_{CO_2}$ equal to 1, and it struck me as rather extraordinary that this should be very close to the sensitivity with plasma, which in our case is $\cdot 8$, I think Dr. Astrup will agree with that figure. It is curious that plasma should give almost the maximum sensitivity.

Severinghaus: Yes. I look upon that as an index that in plasma there are other buffers. If there were no other buffer besides the bicarbonate it would also have a slope of 1. The proteins, however, are buffers and I suppose there are phosphates and other weak electrolytes which dissociate.

Bishop: I was very interested to hear of the stages of your work with the oxygen electrode and to notice how closely they resemble the phases we have been through. We too found the same trouble with a lucite chamber, and then we went on to brass and found the same rapid fall of oxygen tension. Finally we settled upon the stainless steel cuvette. I notice that you still use a lucite tonometer to equilibrate and it is quite thin walled as well.

Severinghaus: It is as thin as we can make it.

Bishop: Do you not find some trouble with diffusion of oxygen from the water bath?

Severinghaus: Well, we are running gas continuously through the inside of the tonometer, and not letting it be stationary and therefore any diffusion would be a secondary phenomenon com-pared with the rate of gas flow.

Bishop: Yes.

Severinghaus: I think a more serious drawback is the tempera-ture problem, because with lucite, if you introduce cold blood in a tonometer it may take 10 to 15 minutes before it warms up, so we have always introduced warm blood. I would like to have a glass tonometer, I think. I do want to see through the wall, but glass I think could be many times better than lucite.

Bishop: I see that you have been using blood to calibrate which, of course, requires a somewhat larger sample. We have used water for the calibrating points, using nitrogen and air as the equilibrating gases. We found that using a magnetic stirrer and a fairly thick membrane we reduced the flow sensitivity to a great extent.

Severinghaus: What is the difference between the water and the gas in your electrode?

Bishop: There is a difference between water and the gas. I cannot give you the figure, but there is very little difference between water and blood.

Severinghaus: You mean there is a difference of the order of 10 per cent?

Bishop: No, less than that. The blood value is about 2–3 per cent below the water value.

Severinghaus: You use thick membranes.

Bishop: Thick membranes—polyethylene, ·005″—and it gives us a response time for 90 per cent of about 3 minutes.

Severinghaus: Do you observe any interference due to zero oxygen background current changing over the course of time being a variable proportion of your total current?

Bishop: No, I do not think we do.

Severinghaus: Our background current with polyethylene runs in the order of 0·1 per cent to 0·3 per cent oxygen equivalent. The transistor amplifier has a screw-driven control for backing off the zero oxygen current, so that the response is linear from zero and can be read directly from the dial.

Wright: There is only one thing I would like to ask and that is, do you get any trouble with hæmolysis from your second stirrer?

Severinghaus: Well, I have not measured it, but I think we do. I do not know what the effect of that is.

Wright: It might have some effect since the characteristics of hæmoglobin depend on its concentration.

Severinghaus: What would you expect it to do, make the P_{O_2} go up or down? Someone once said that the oxygen consumption of red cells suddenly went up at the time of hæmolysis. Do you know whether that is true?

Wright: No, I don't know that.

Severinghaus: Others said this could not possibly be.

Wright: I think I would expect it to let the P_{O_2} go down.

Severinghaus: Well, it in fact does go down quite rapidly, but as I mentioned this morning after Dr. Nunn's paper, if you remove the white cells it stops going down. Most of our oxygen consumption in the cuvette I think is due to white cells. When the blood is completely saturated, that is with a P_{O_2} of around 600, with this particular system the rate of fall of oxygen tension amounts to 3 or 4 per cent per minute, in fresh blood. If you remove the white cells it is less than 1 per cent per minute.

Wright: There is one other thing I would like to ask and that is how long does your tonometer take to bring blood to equilibrium?

Severinghaus: I do not know for sure, but if you put in warm blood which is already oxygenated and you are equilibrating it with air it seems to be ready in about 5 minutes, but we ordinarily run about 15 minutes. Water equilibrates faster of course.

Wright: I was fascinated by Dr. Astrup's method of equilibrating blood in 1 minute.

Severinghaus: I think he has a much more rapid stirring arrangement than we do. Practically no volume of blood is unexposed as soon as it starts.

Mattock: There is one little point which is rather interesting, although it probably is not important. I am interested in the Clark electrode with straight silver chloride wires using saturated KCl, in which with an ordinary electrode system operating virtually at zero current null point reading, one would get considerable drift.

Severinghaus: Potential drift at the silver reference electrode will not materially alter the current since the polarograph is operated on a current plateau.

Mattock: Probably in this case you would be helping by the fact that you are making it anodic, but it might be a secondary process which could contribute and cause a certain amount of difficulty. It would be rather interesting to know if it would have any effect. All you do is throw in some silver chloride.

Severinghaus: Well, the drift in this of course would have to be current drift. In other words, it would have to change the resistance of the silver chloride wire and the direction of the current is such, I think, that you are always plating silver chloride on to the silver.

Mattock: Yes, you tend to improve it by making it anodic. It may not be serious in practice.

Severinghaus: What happens to a silver chloride wire when you get all the available silver covered with chloride? Does its resistance go away up?

Mattock: It goes up, yes.

Severinghaus: Then what should you do?

Mattock: Well, the point is, you have got that situation and you want to retain it, don't you?

Severinghaus: If you have a big resistance then you get a drop in current at the high oxygen end of the curve, due to covering of the silver wire with chloride.

Mattock: Ah, you mean continuing to deposit silver chloride on the silver?

Severinghaus: Yes.

Mattock: Well, I would say, and I think Mr. Lauchlan would agree, that it is probably unlikely that you would get a very heavy deposition on there beyond a certain stage.

Lauchlan: With that small current one would get a very small deposit.

Mattock: Yes.

Severinghaus: Well, I am just tinkering with the idea that perhaps it is the saturated KCl which keeps us from getting into the problem of the high resistance electrode, because it keeps dissolving the precipitate as soon as it is formed.

Mattock: It may be achieving some equilibrium in just this way. I don't know. It is just an interesting point which struck me when I saw that thing happening.

Severinghaus: I had not thought about this before, but in fact if you do have a significant voltage drop across the silver chloride layer then you again have a non-linear electrode at high oxygen tension.

Wright: The resistance of chloride films is very intimately dependent on the nature of the crystal structure of the silver chloride, and may vary by a factor of about ten times. It is of the order of, I think, 200 to 1,000 ohms, from $0 \cdot 1$ cms^2.

Mattock: That depends on the thickness, doesn't it? It can be a lot less though.

Severinghaus: Then it probably would not contribute error at all.

Mattock: What sort of resistance drop do you have?

Severinghaus: Well, I do not know because the electrode itself, of course, has a variable resistance depending on oxygen tension and I suppose the way to measure it would be either to use it at much higher voltage, or else to use it at an extremely high oxygen tension and find out where it began to fall off due to the resistance of that pathway.

Wright: You would try half a volt?

Severinghaus: Yes.

Wright: And what current do you get?

Severinghaus: Well, it depends on the oxygen tension. Let's say with pure oxygen in this electrode with polyethylene, 5 microamps. What you are going to be calculating is the resistance of the electrode, you see, including the platinum. It will not tell us about the KCl bridge. And you are measuring the resistance at the platinum surface between platinum and KCl due to the fact that you have a polarized electrode.

Lauchlan: Did you have to take particular care to thermostat your transistor amplifier? So many of them are better thermometers than amplifiers.

Severinghaus: Well, we did two things. We put a thermistor in as a load resistor which compensates for some of the thermal drift. We mounted the two transistors together inside a little plastic tube which keeps their temperature from changing much. It does drift after being turned on, but it is a null-balanced device and you just keep going back and forth with the switch between the null ground and the null looking at the electrode current.

Chairman: When I was in Baltimore 18 months' ago Sheppard showed me an oxygen electrode which he had got into a needle, whose gauge I cannot remember, but the insertion of which into an artery would not have filled me with dismay.

Severinghaus: It goes through an 18-gauge needle.

Chairman: And can one, by this means, get a reliable continuous reading of intra-arterial oxygen tension?

Severinghaus: Well, that is the electrode that I referred to as being made by Beckman. They have produced several. Only a few people have one, and I believe the problem is one of uncontrollable drift. It is a problem of working with tiny little things. You have to put a very tiny polyethylene cap on top of the electrode inside of an 18-gauge needle and that is not easy. You have the additional problem of calibration. You have to calibrate it in some sort of a device and then put it into the artery and assume that it does not change. It may possibly turn out to be usable.

Chairman: It is an easier problem, I suppose, to push a needle into tissue and get intra-muscular oxygen tensions, for example, because you can use a bigger needle. And then one has the problem of whether the oxygen tension there is representative of even a closely adjacent part.

Severinghaus: The bigger the needle you put in the more the distortion of the tissues you cause, too. Perhaps local ischæmia or something like that.

Wynn: What is the purpose of the continuous oxygen tension reading?

Severinghaus: To be up to date!

Wynn: If you think of the possible number of uses for it, there are so many possible solutions which could be different from putting a needle into an artery that I would have thought that an electrode inside a needle inside an artery would not have much future.

Severinghaus: I agree. Furthermore you have the problem that your artery is never at 38 degrees.

Wynn: Can I now ask you, Dr. Severinghaus: these two electrodes which you have described, would you say that they were suitable for clinical use in a random sort of way? That is to say, supposing they had not been in use for two weeks could you come in in the middle of the night and use them quickly?

Severinghaus: No. I do not think so.

Wynn: Have you even approached the stage where that might be possible?

Severinghaus: Well, assuming that the membrane does not have a hole in it when you come in in the middle of the night, it will work all right. And assuming the person who does it is good at it, it might well do the job. I am sure that if I myself were to go in in the middle of the night and turned the thing on I could get a reasonably good answer from it. We have an instrument in the chemistry lab. kept at 37° and one of our technicians can do analyses on it without much notice.

Campbell: I was just thinking that, although this morning I was preaching the policy of simplicity, if in fact I had a device which would give me continuous record of the P_{CO_2} and of the P_{O_2} and I could sit in a chair and move a knob which altered the treadmill and move a knob which altered the inspired oxygen concentration and read the P_{O_2} and P_{CO_2} I could tell you an awful lot about somebody's lungs. But you would have to know the physiology. You would not just get it from a shiny machine. You would have to know the physiology.

Nunn: Teflon, you say, is highly permeable to CO_2 but not to hydrogen ions. I always imagined that hydrogen ions were the most mobile of ions being the smallest, but this is not so, apparently.

Severinghaus: The hydrogen ion is charged and the oxygen is not and it is an electrical phenomenon of repulsion, I guess. You get one hydrogen down somewhere inside the teflon and the only electrical field is produced by it, and it repels all the rest of the hydrogen ions back into the solution, I guess. There is another way of looking at it. There is nothing in that in which it can combine and you go through neutral, because the water cannot get into it.

Wright: You carry a very high surface charge on these plastic films.

Severinghaus: That is another way of saying the same thing. Presumably the holes are plenty big. And hydrogen gas, I suppose, would go through very easily, although I have not tried this.

Nunn: You can measure the rate of CO_2 passing through these films by direct measurement with a burette and mercury.

Severinghaus: Yes. I had the idea that nitrogen did not go through nearly as well as oxygen, without having measured it.

Mattock: On purely steric grounds it should do.

Severinghaus: It should go through faster?

Mattock: Oh, yes, For purely steric reasons.

Severinghaus: Oxygen certainly goes through rubber. Well, CO_2 is a different problem in rubber, isn't it? CO_2 goes through rubber better than nitrogen and oxygen. Is that a solution in rubber?

Mattock: Maybe so. Nitrogen is quite small, actually. It is also far less polar than oxygen is.

Wright: What about CO_2?

Mattock: CO_2 is bigger than either of them, isn't it?

Severinghaus: It certainly goes through both polyethylene and teflon several times faster than oxygen.

Mattock: I think it is a bit more than a steric reason: something a bit more specific than that.

Wright: It also goes very easily through cell membranes.

Mattock: Of course, it may be residual. It may be popping from one little interstice to another.

Chairman: Is the transfer of CO_2 from a membrane affected by the presence of water?

Severinghaus: Yes. It certainly is in biological systems. It is thought to go through in solution.

Chairman: And if there is a little film of water on the membrane we are considering it would presumably have some effect on the rate of transfer.

Wright: Do these plastic films contain any water at all?

Severinghaus: I do not think teflon will. I am sure that the molecular physicist would say, yes there must be some water. Teflon is very hydrophobic.

Nunn: Polyethylene does contain water but the amount of water is less in such materials as nylon.

Severinghaus: Nylon does take up water and swell.

Nunn: But less than polyethylene.

XI. THE VALUE OF THE END-TIDAL SAMPLE

P. W. Ramwell, B.Sc., Ph.D.

Research Assistant, Department of Anæsthesia, University of Leeds

On examining the programme for this meeting it was obvious that to-day end-tidal sampling would probably be buried without trace. Dr. Severinghaus already has dug a deep hole and Dr. Campbell has begun the burying. Nevertheless it is proposed to discuss some of the uses to which end-tidal sampling can be put.

There are three points I would like to make at the beginning of this paper. Firstly, though the end-tidal sample has many uses in physiology it is proposed to limit the discussion of its value strictly to the field of clinical medicine. Secondly, the degree of precision with which the end-tidal, or any other method of alveolar gas sample, can be employed to estimate the arterial CO_2 tension, will be regarded as the main criterion in discussing the method. Finally, the term " alveolar air " will be used in this context to describe gas which has come from the alveoli, whether the latter are poorly perfused or poorly ventilated, and whether overperfused or overventilated. When it is necessary to employ a more precise definition of " alveolar air " then the appropriate adjective can be added.

It is worthwhile recalling some of the advantages and disadvantages of arterial sampling and end-tidal sampling. Arterial puncture is not always easy and to obtain a good sample with a fine needle and without a local anæsthetic requires a fair amount of skill. Our chairman has already commented on the rigmarole of arterial sampling. Except for the P_{CO_2} electrode of Stow and Randall (1954) which is not widely used at present, the methods of blood gas analysis require careful training of technicians, as this meeting testifies, and considerable skill on their part. Skilled technicians will always be at a premium. If one can replace the laboratory equipment and technician by apparatus which may be operated by a registrar, and which can give a reasonable estimate of the arterial CO_2 tension at the bedside, so much the better.

From the patient's point of view, especially if he is conscious and being artificially ventilated, it is hardly likely that he will welcome repetitive arterial punctures or an indwelling catheter which may be left in an artery for as long as two weeks. (Astrup, 1956.)

Though lung gas sampling methods and CO_2 analysis can prove a useful guide to the clinician it is important that two aspects should be clearly appreciated.

(1) Any gas sampling method to be used in clinical medicine must be virtually foolproof. The method of choice is the continuous one which necessitates a fast response CO_2

TABLE I. *Some Values of the Alveolar-Arterial CO_2 Difference as Determined by " Spot " Sampling Procedures*

Type of gas sample	A.a difference	Reference
H.P. e.e. . . .	− 0·5	Bock *et al.* (1924)
e.e.	+ 0·48	Field *et al.* (1925)
e.e.	+ 0·85	Richards *et al.* (1928)
e.e.	+ 0·2	Bock *et al.* (1929)
e.e.	+ 0·7	Dill *et al.* (1931)
H.P. e.i. . . .	− 4·1	Riley *et al.* (1946)
H.P. e.e. . . .	+ 1·0	Galdston *et al.* (1947)
H.P. e.e. . . .	+ 1·8	Barker *et al.* (1949)
H.P. e.i. . . .	− 0·2	Barker *et al.* (1949)
Rahn	+ 1·9	Barker *et al.* (1949)
Rahn	+ 0·2	Suskind *et al.* (1950)
H.P. e.i. . . .	− 0·2	Lambertsen (1954)
e.e.	+ 1·9	Lambertsen (1954)
Tracheal . . .	0	Lambertsen (1954)
Rahn	0	Galdston *et al.* (1951)
Rahn	+ 0·6	Saxton (1953)
Rahn	+ 0·9	Carter (1954)
Rahn	+ 2·0	Lambertsen (1954)
e.e.	+ 2·0	Asmussen *et al.* (1956)

H.P. e.e.   *denotes Haldane Priestley end-expiratory samples*
H.P. e.i.   ,,   *Haldane Priestley end-inspiratory samples*
Rahn   ,,   *Rahn end-tidal samples*
Tracheal   ,,   *Sample taken from trachea*

analyser. Where intermittent positive pressure respiration is employed, with or without a negative phase and with or without patient triggering devices, a " spot " or " snatch " gas sampling method is likely to lead to erroneous results. Where different gas mixtures are used for ventilating the patient as in anæsthesia, care needs to be taken to ensure that the infra-red CO_2 analyser or fast response katharometer (Visser, 1957) are adequately calibrated (Ramwell and Dawson, 1958).

(2) The second aspect is that wherever possible the end-tidal or end-plateau tensions should be checked against simultaneously drawn arterial blood under the actual clinical conditions where one wishes to use the technique.

The first table has been drawn up to recall something of the effort that has been put into the task of justifying the use of lung gas sampling methods in the past. The list is by no means definitive but it will be seen that in most cases the mean alveolar-arterial CO_2 difference is relatively small. However it should be clearly understood that the majority of the figures refer to comparisons on young healthy subjects.

Because the alveolar CO_2 plateau has a slope of about 0.1 per cent CO_2 per second in this type of subject, it is not of crucial importance at which part of the plateau a particular sampling device acts. For example, if we accept Dubois, Britt and Fenn's (1952) conclusions that the mid-point of the plateau corresponds to the arterial CO_2 tension, then the end-tidal sampling device of Rahn (1949) will introduce a clinically negligible discrepancy.

As a physiologist I would not wish to advise the clinician on the *value* of the " alveolar " gas sample in medicine. However, I can describe the three different circumstances in which the infra-red technique has been employed at Leeds and will rely upon the clinicians present at this meeting to draw their own conclusions.

Some of the results obtained for the end-plateau/arterial CO_2 difference when fractional sampling and rapid infra-red analysis is used can be seen in Table II. From these results one may conclude that the method provides a fairly reasonable estimate of the arterial CO_2 tension.

The first circumstance I would like to mention is the use of the infra-red technique in long term artificial respiration.

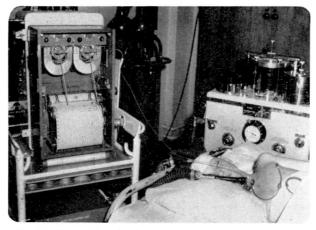

Fig. 1. A subject undergoing intermittent positive pressure respiration in the treatment for tetanus. In the foreground is a twin channel fast response Evershed and Vignoles recorder, one channel of which is recording the electrical output of an infra-red CO_2 analyser.

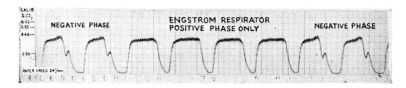

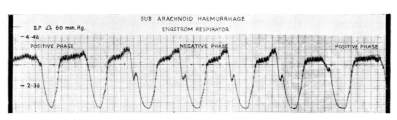

Fig. 2. The effect of the application of a negative phase on the alveolar CO_2 plateau at the end of expiration. The top trace was obtained during surgical anæsthesia and the bottom trace is of a subject being ventilated after a subarachnoid hæmorrhage.

To face p. 152.

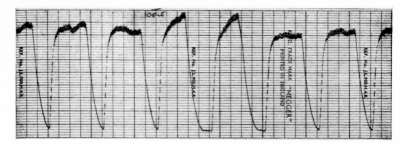

FIG. 3. The effect on the end plateau P_{CO_2} of sternal pressure at the end of expiration. The patient was undergoing treatment in the Tetanus Unit.

FIG. 4. The Kolff type of artificial kidney in current use at Leeds.

(Reproduced by courtesy of the Editor, Leeds Medical School Journal)

TABLE II. *Alveolar-Arterial CO_2 Differences Using the Rapid Infra-Red Method in Conscious Healthy Subjects*

	Mean	S.D.	Number	Reference
Infants	0·3	3·14	18	Stahlman *et al.* (1957)
Adults	0·6	—	18	Saxton (1953)
Adults	1·6	3·7	10	Ramwell (1959)
Adults (breathing air) .	0·9	3·0	10	Severinghaus *et al.* (1957)
Adults (breathing O_2) .	3·6	2·0	7	Severinghaus *et al.* (1957)
Adults (breathing air slowly)	1·4	2·1	6	Severinghaus *et al.* (1957)
Aged (78·4 ± 6·2 years) .	1·3	—	18	Tenney *et al.* (1956)

Much of the credit for the validation of the infra-red method under these circumstances is due to Collier, Affeldt and Farr (1955) who published some of the results illustrated in Table III. It would seem that fractional sampling is better than total expiratory sampling.

TABLE III. *Alveolar-Arterial CO_2 Differences Using the Rapid Infra-Red Method in Polio Subjects and Patients with Serious Lung and Heart Disease*

Method	Mean	S.D.	S.E.	Number	Reference
Continuous fractional sampling . . .	+0·9	1·8	0·4	22	Collier *et al.* (1955)
Continuous total expiratory sampling .	+3·2	2·4	0·6	19	Collier *et al.* (1955)
Continuous fractional sampling . . .	+2·8	4·1	1·1	15	Collier (1956)

It is interesting that in 15 patients with serious lung and heart disease, Collier (1956) found the mean alveolar-arterial CO_2 difference to be only three times greater than in the first group of 22 subjects undergoing artificial respiration. Our experience in Leeds has been confined to the Tetanus Unit where approximately 25 patients have been treated. Fig. 1 illustrates one of the two boys being treated at the moment. The treatment includes induced muscular paralysis and intermittent positive pressure respiration with air. Most subjects have an end-plateau P_{CO_2} of about 35 mm. Hg.

In a disease which is as wasting and ravaging as tetanus, one of the important things is to minimize the changes in the blood electrolytes. By ventilating the patient and keeping to a constant end-plateau P_{CO_2} it is hoped to eliminate one of the variables which may affect the acid-base balance and blood pressure (Ablett, 1956).

The infra-red technique is also useful in teaching, for sometimes it is not appreciated that when the body temperature rises, the respirator needs adjusting to blow off the CO_2 being produced by increased metabolism. In practice, where hyperpyrexia occurs, surface cooling is often employed.

The application of a negative phase during expiration (Fig. 2) or by pressure on the chest (Fig. 3) can markedly elevate the end-tidal P_{CO_2}. This tends to occur in the older patient or when physiotherapy has not prevented changes within the lungs.

The second use to which we have put the infra-red technique is during hæmodialysis with the artificial kidney (Fig. 4). This apparatus not only removes urea, excess potassium and acid metabolites but it also arterializes the blood with respect to oxygen. Whether CO_2 is unloaded or not depends on the P_{CO_2} under the transparent cover. The use of the kidney (Fig. 5) as an extracorporeal circulation is limited as the blood flow

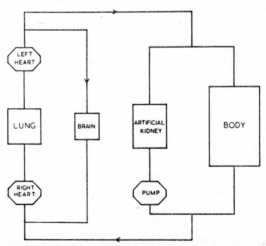

FIG. 5. Diagram showing the artificial kidney as an " extra corporeal " circulation. By this method 0·5 litres of blood per minute can be arterialized.

is only about 300 to 500 ml./minute. For all practical purposes the artificial kidney can be regarded as being in parallel across the body.

We have been following the response of the respiratory centre to a sudden change in buffer base (Parsons and Ramwell, 1959). Fig. 6 illustrates the end-plateau and arterial CO_2 changes when the buffer base is sharply increased. In about one-third of the 42 cases investigated, there is little change in the P_{CO_2} during hæmodialysis despite marked changes in pH. As one would expect however, there are considerable changes in the minute volume. The discrepancy between the end-plateau and arterial CO_2 tensions next day is due to the difficulty

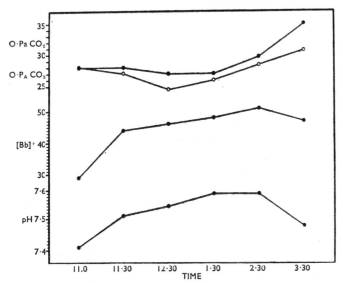

FIG. 6. Acid-base and end-plateau P_{CO_2} changes during hæmodialysis.

in persuading a restless, talkative patient to lie quietly and breathe steadily. For the purposes of this investigation we are primarily interested in using the infra-red technique to save the considerable labour involved in arterial blood gas analysis.

The third circumstance to be discussed is that of anæsthesia. Very careful preliminary work led us to believe that the end-expiratory P_{CO_2} during anæsthesia was sometimes far lower than one would expect from the arterial P_{CO_2}. It was interesting to examine the results of Buckley and his colleagues (1952) which quite clearly show a definite " alveolar "-arterial CO_2 difference at tensions below 70 mm. Hg. In Table IV I have

TABLE IV. *Alveolar-Arterial CO_2 Difference in Intubated Subjects during Anæsthesia*

Reference	State of Patient	Mean	S.D.	Number
Buckley *et al.* (1952)		(approx.) 6 to 7	—	15
Severinghaus *et al.* (1957) . . .	Conscious	2·1	1·8	4
	A.R.	4·4	2·3	5
	A.R. (Chest open)	6·1	1·6	5
	End of operation	8·1	3·0	5
Ramwell (1959) .	Conscious	1·6	3·7	10
	S.R. and A.R. (End-plateau)	5·0	3·6	9
	A.R. (End-expiratory)	4·9	4·4	8
Nunn (1958) . .	S.R.	4·46	2·52	11
	A.R.	4·72	2·47	12
	A.R. (Chest open)	6·0	5·57	6

A.R.—Artificial respiration. S.R.—Spontaneous respiration.

estimated the difference to be about 6 to 7 mm. Hg. Subsequently we measured differences of 5·0 and 4·9 mm. Hg using end-plateau and end-expiratory methods respectively. These results are largely in agreement with Nunn (1958) and with Severinghaus (1957) (Table IV).

Fig. 7 illustrates a typical result from a patient anæsthetized with 21-hydroxydione sodium succinate. The end-expiratory arterial CO_2 difference was 9·0 and 9·4 mm. Hg respectively. This result is quite typical though a better idea of the constant CO_2 difference can be gained from Fig. 8. This patient received chloropromazine and thiopentone and throughout the experiment he was ventilated at a rate of 18 per minute; only the tidal volume was changed. In this case the " alveolar " values are end-plateau tensions.

There is general agreement that the CO_2 differences represent the formation of an " alveolar dead space " due to wide distributions of the ventilation to perfusion ratios. The cause is a matter for speculation at the present moment. It is interesting that all patients studied by all the investigators were intubated. In the last year, Daly and Daly (1958) have demonstrated the

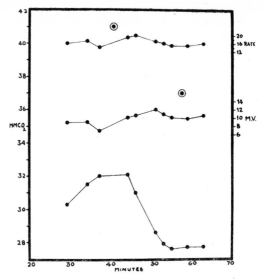

FIG. 7. End-expiratory and arterial CO_2 tensions in a fully curarized subject during anæsthesia. The large circles represent arterial CO_2 tensions. The subject was ventilated by a constant volume hand pump, the stroke of which was decreased after the first arterial sample.

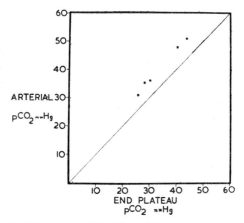

FIG. 8. End-plateau/arterial CO_2 differences measured during anæsthesia. The subject was ventilated with an Engstrom respirator, the rate of which was kept constant; only the tidal volume was varied.

presence of pulmonary vasodepressor fibres in the dog and Helen Duke (1958) has demonstrated the existence of pulmonary vasoconstrictor fibres in the superior cervical ganglion of the cat. One is left wondering whether intubation or anæsthetic procedures cause uneven distribution of the alveolar capillary blood through nervous reflex action.

In conclusion it must be admitted that the value of the end-tidal sample as a clinical tool is limited to the conscious subject free of cardiovascular and respiratory disease.

Acknowledgments

I am grateful to Dr. J. J. L. Ablett of the Tetanus Unit, to Dr. F. M. Parsons of the M.R.C. Metabolic Disturbances During Surgery Unit and to Dr. R. P. Harbord, Reader in Anæsthesia, for providing facilities for this work. The research was supported in part by a grant from the Medical Research Council.

REFERENCES

ABLETT, J. J. L. (1956). Tetanus and the Anæsthetist. A Review of the Symptomatology and the Recent Advances in Treatment. *Brit. J. Anæsth.*, **28**, 258.

ASMUSSEN, E., and NIELSEN, A. (1956). Physiological Dead Space and Alveolar Gas Pressures at Rest and during Muscular Exercise. *Acta physiol. scand.*, **38**, 1.

ASTRUP, P. (1956). In Lassen, H. C. A., *Management of Life Threatening Poliomyelitis.* Edinburgh, E. and S. Livingstone, p. 111.

BARKER, E. S., PONTIUS, R. G., AVIADO, D. M., and LAMBERTSEN, C. J. (1949). Simultaneous Comparisons of Alveolar Gas Tensions obtained by Various Sampling Methods. *Amer. J. med. Sci.*, 217, 708.

BOCK, A. V., DILL, D. B., EDWARDS, H. T., HENDERSON, L. J., and TALBOTT, J. H. (1929). On the Partial Pressures of Oxygen and Carbon Dioxide in Arterial Blood and Alveolar Air. *J. Physiol.*, **68**, 277.

BOCK, A. V., and FIELD, H. (1924). The Carbon Dioxide Equilibrium in Alveolar Air and Arterial Blood. *J. biol. Chem.*, **62**, 269.

BUCKLEY, J. J., VAN BERGEN, F. H., HEMINGWAY, A., DEMOREST, H. L., MILLER, F. A., KNIGHT, R. T., and VARCO, R. L. (1952). A Portable Mass Spectrometer for Continuous Alveolar Gas Analysis: Certain Technical Considerations Inherent in its Use. *Anesthesiology*, **13**, 455.

CARTER, E. T. (1954). Personal Communication to H. Rahn in Handbook of Respiratory Physiology. U.S.A.F., Randolph Base, Texas.

COLLIER, C. R. (1956). Determination of Mixed Venous Carbon Dioxide Tensions by Rebreathing. *J. appl. Physiol.*, **9**, 25.

COLLIER, C. R., AFFELDT, J. E., and FARR, A. F. (1955). Continuous Rapid Infra-red Carbon Dioxide Analysis. Fractional Sampling and Accuracy in determining Alveolar Carbon Dioxide. *J. Lab. clin. Med.*, **45**, 256.

DALY, I. DE BURGH, and DALY, M. DE BURGH (1958). Pulmonary Vasodilator Fibres. *J. Physiol.*, **142**, 19 p.

DILL, D. B., EDWARDS, H. T., FOLLING, A., OBERG, S. A., PAPPENHEIMER, A. M., and TALBOTT, J. H. (1931). Adaptations of the Organism to Changes in Oxygen Pressure. *J. Physiol.*, **71**, 47.

DUBOIS, A. B., BRITT, A. G., and FENN, W. O. (1952). Alveolar Carbon Dioxide during the Respiratory Cycle. *J. appl. Physiol.*, **4**, 535.

DUKE, HELEN (1958). Pulmonary Vasoconstrictor Fibres in the Stellate Ganglion of the Cat. *J. Physiol.* (*in press*).

FIELD, H. Jr., BOCK, A. V., GILDEA, E. F., and LATHROP, F. L. (1925). Rate of Circulation of the Blood in Normal Resting Individuals. *J. clin. Invest.*, **1**, 65.

GALDSTON, M., BENJAMIN, B., and HUREWITZ, M. (1951). " Alveolar " Air and Arterial Blood Gas Tension Studies in Normal and Chronic Lung Disease Patients. *Fed. Proc.*, **10**, 47.

GALDSTON, M., and WOLLACK, A. C. (1947). Oxygen and Carbon Dioxide Tensions of Alveolar Air and Arterial Blood in Healthy Young Adults at Rest and after Exercise. *Amer. J. Physiol.*, **151**, 276.

HARBORD, R. P., and RAMWELL, P. W. (1958). The " Alveolar "-Arterial CO_2 Gradient during Anæsthesia. *J. Physiol.*, **142**, 61P.

LAMBERTSEN, C. J. (1954). Personal Communication to H. Rahn in Handbook of Respiratory Physiology, U.S.A.F., Randolph Base, Texas.

NUNN, J. F. (1958). Ph.D. Thesis. University of Birmingham.

PARSONS, F. M., and RAMWELL, P. W. (1959). Acid Base Balance during Hæmodialysis. In preparation.

RAHN, H., and OTIS, A. B. (1949). Continuous Analysis of Alveolar Gas Composition during Work, Hyperpnea, Hypercapnia and Anoxia. *J. appl. Physiol.*, **1**, 717.

RAMWELL, P. W. (1959). Lung Gas Sampling and Analysis during Anæsthesia: In *Symposium on Pulmonary Ventilation.* Manchester, Sherratt and Son.

RAMWELL, P. W., and DAWSON, J. B. (1958). The Calibration of Infrared Gas Analyser for Use in the Estimation of Carbon Dioxide. *Phys. in Med. Biol.*, **2**, 280.

RICHARDS, D. W., and STRAUSS, M. L. (1928). Circulatory Adjustment in Anæmia. *J. clin. Invest.*, **5**, 161.

RILEY, R. L., LILIENTHALL, J. L., PROEMMEL, D. D., and FRANKE, R. E. (1946). On the Effective Determination of the Physiologically Effective Pressures of Oxygen and Carbon Dioxide in Alveolar Air. *Amer. J. Physiol.*, **147**, 191.

SAXTON, G. A. (1953). Method for Sampling and Analysing Alveolar P_{CO_2}. *Fed. Proc.*, **12**, 125.

SEVERINGHAUS, J. W., STUPFEL, M. A., and BRADLEY, A. F. (1957). Alveolar Dead Space and Arterial to end Tidal Carbon Dioxide Difference during Hypothermia in Dog and Man. *J. appl. Physiol.*, **10**, 349.

STAHLMAN, M. T., MEECE, N. J. (1957). Pulmonary Ventilation and Diffusion in the Human Newborn Infant. *J. clin. Invest.*, **36**, 1081.

STOW, R. W., and RANDALL, BARBARA F. (1954). Electrical Measurement of the P_{CO_2} of Blood. *Amer. J. Physiol.*, **179**, 678.

SUSKIND, M., BRUCE, A. R., MCDOWELL, M. E., YU, P. N. G., and LOVEJOY, F. W. (1950). Normal Variations in End Tidal Air and Arterial Blood Carbon Dioxide and Oxygen Tensions during Moderate Exercise. *J. appl. Physiol.*, 3, 282.

TENNEY, S. M., and STERN, E. A. (1956). Interpretation of Respiratory Drug Effects in Man. *Anesthesiology*, 17, 82.

VISSER, B. F. (1957). Clinical Gas Analysis based on Thermal Conductivity. Thesis, University of Utrecht. Holland.

DISCUSSION

Chairman: I think Dr. Ramwell's paper may have done something at any rate to delay the interment of the end-tidal sample. Dr. Harbord, you have been associated with Dr. Ramwell in some of this work, would you like to comment on his paper?

Harbord: Although we have done a great deal in developing these methods I have not yet reached the stage when I use end-tidal samples to help in the administration of anæsthesia. The end-tidal sample cannot be used to estimate arterial P_{CO_2} although, if it remains constant, a steady ventilatory state appears probable. End expiratory P_{CO_2} measurement may be valuable in assessing the patient's ventilation in the immediate post-operative period when spontaneous respiration has returned after full curarization. I do not think I am yet in a position to assess reliably the value of this method.

Chairman: I think a good many of us find ourselves in a similar state. I was interested to see the effect on the trace of the negative pressure phase coming in. Can you or Dr. Ramwell account for this?

Harbord: I cannot.

Ramwell: I would rather pass the ball over to Dr. Campbell. I think he is better qualified.

Campbell: Well, I am going to pull something out of the air and say that you may get a column of air from that portion of dead space which is, in fact, the last to empty and which has not come up before anyway and you just jerk some of that up with it. You would only have to get a relatively small volume of actual stream sucked up from the dead space.

Ramwell: Do you think it is actually from underventilated areas which has been pulled out by the negative phase and the pressure on the chest?

Campbell: I think it is just air which is down there and which has not come up before. The concept of series and parallel is very useful as a thought, but in fact when things are going on in patients who have disordered distribution, you cannot draw a line and say where you had a series and where you had a parallel dead space. In fact where you draw your line is a function of your technique, very largely, and you may have gas which has come from parts of the lung which have a relatively low ventilation/perfusion ratio, or you may just have it coming from parts of the lung which have got perfectly adequate ventilation/perfusion ratio but is coming late.

Sykes: This is the sort of picture that Hugh-Jones and West have seen when obstructing one bronchus in dogs. The lobe supplied by the obstructed bronchus empties a little later than the rest of the lungs.

Campbell: Yes. You get the situation, of course, in which the first part of the lung to fill is the best ventilated part of the lung. However, as it fills with the dead space it is the worst ventilated part of the lung—if you take it to the ridiculous extreme.

If one has a normal subject and one wants to follow a change in arterial CO_2 tension, and one wants to do it quickly breath by breath, then end-tidal sample with a rapid analyser is the best thing we have. If you are quite sure that you are having a constant relationship between the end-tidal and the arterial sample it is also a very convenient method of doing it. But if you have the problem of deciding just what somebody's arterial CO_2 tension is, as opposed to whether it is changing, I do not think that the end-tidal can continue to have a serious place because it is less reliable and it is more difficult. Now there is nobody who has used the method more effectively and more extensively, really, than Collier in fact did, is there? I did not know whether to show this slide this morning or not. I was not sure whether to be nasty before Dr. Ramwell gave his paper or to throw a stick at him afterwards. I could not decide which was the better and as time was short I kept this slide back. It shows (Fig. 9) how the rebreathing method compares with measured arterial CO_2 tension. And here (Fig. 3, p. 125) is the slide you have seen this morning, comparing the end-tidal method with the measured value. You will see two patients who had CO_2 tensions of 70 or over but with the end-tidal method one showed a value of 40. I think clinically that would be very misleading. These were the same patients.

Ramwell: I think we all agree with what Dr. Campbell has just said. I would like to make my own personal position more clear. As a physiologist I am only interested in healthy young people. Wherever there is disease, when a patient comes with diseased lungs to the artificial kidney, I pack my bags and go. I find life far too complicated in dealing with subjects with healthy lungs. I do think the end-tidal sample has much value in clinical medicine as such. It may be useful in specific projects, such as the hæmo-dialysis project for following the arterial CO_2 tension.

I was most interested to hear that this morning Dr. Macrae said he found the end-tidal sample of no value at all in his polio patients.

Macrae: Very little, clinically.

Ramwell: And yet we have these figures of Collier, Affeldt and Farr.

Macrae: They are accurate as long as the lung is normal. If there is something wrong, then end-tidal samples are not very much use. We have noticed that your plateau can be easily sampled from the normal lung. A sample can be taken more or less anywhere along the plateau, but when there is something wrong with the lungs there is a gradient, not a plateau. You are liable to snatch maybe from the bottom of the gradient and have very little CO_2, or from the top of the gradient and have a lot; and one never really knows where you are getting the sample from.

Severinghaus: I think it would be unfortunate if we went on record as saying the end-tidal sample had no value in clinical

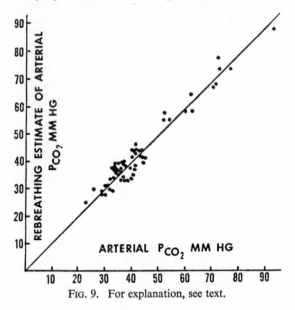

FIG. 9. For explanation, see text.

medicine, because clinical medicine is not interested only in what the arterial P_{CO_2} is. It is also interested in what is wrong with the lungs, and I think that there are a number of things which can be learned from the end-tidal sample, in conjunction with an arterial sample, about the pulmonary physiology. This is, of course, not a conference on pulmonary physiology, but I might say that the things that we have been interested in, by measuring both arterial and end-tidal samples—as have Dr. Nunn, Dr. Ramwell and, I think, a good many others—have really to do with the distribution of blood flow through the lungs. If you can imagine one half of the lung as having no blood flow at all, the gas which is ventilated into that lung will not receive CO_2 from the blood because there is not any blood, and it will be expelled into the expired air and will dilute the gas coming from the other lung down to approximately half of its CO_2 concentration, so the end-tidal sample then would be much lower, in fact about half that of the arterial blood. And except for the fact that the unperfused lung breathes some of the dead space gas, it would be exactly half, and one can make a pretty good approximation of how much of the lung fails to have blood flow, by this arterial-to-alveolar CO_2 difference. It is best expressed as the ratio of the difference over the arterial CO_2 tension. And this difference is perhaps a good clinical index of pulmonary embolism and that is one of the things that several of us are interested in studying in the near future. And it may also tell us

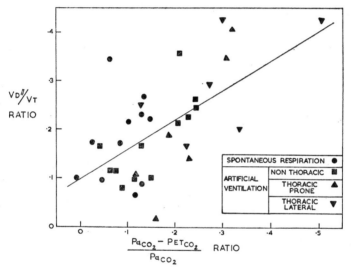

Fig. 10. For explanation, see text.

something about the control of distribution of blood through the lung. The figures which Dr. Ramwell showed about the effect of breathing oxygen on CO_2 difference mean to me that the distribution of blood flow through the lung is normally controlled by the oxygen tension in the pulmonary capillary, and when you breathe oxygen you cause a relaxation of all the vessels in the lung, and gravity then controls the distribution of the blood flow, some areas, being higher in the lung, getting less, and those being lower getting more blood flow.

Nunn: In a number of patients we measured the arterial to end-tidal P_{CO_2} difference, and at the same time measured the physiological dead space and the anatomical dead space. The abscissa here (Fig. 10) is the arterial to end-tidal difference divided by the arterial CO_2 tension expressed as a ratio, and the ordinate is the parallel dead space, that is physiological minus anatomical, divided by tidal volume. In each case we have a ratio which expresses, I think, the ventilation of unperfused spaces. Now, those points actually have a coefficient of correlation of ·59, which is $3\frac{1}{2}$ times its standard error and, I think, significant. Thus we have a method, in the arterial to end-tidal P_{CO_2} difference, which would appear to be reasonably satisfactory for demonstrating the ventilation of unperfused spaces. It is certainly a good deal easier than measuring the physiological and the anatomical dead space simultaneously. I believe that the end-tidal P_{CO_2} may still be a valuable measurement during anæsthesia. I have known it indicate quite unequivocally failure of the CO_2 absorption in rebreathing techniques. On one occasion an unexplained fall in the end-tidal P_{CO_2} indicated a cardiac arrest—fortunately temporary. It is also particularly valuable after long operations in which artificial ventilation has been used. It is satisfying to see the patient return to the ward with an end-tidal P_{CO_2} within safe limits and preferably falling as he recovers from the effects of the anæsthetic drugs. The end-tidal P_{CO_2} is also valuable for teaching. The effects of various drugs on respiration are very clearly shown. It is important, however, to stress that in emphysema the end-tidal P_{CO_2} may differ markedly from the arterial tension and the results will therefore probably be quite misleading, and even potentially dangerous.

Harbord: I should like to speak again. In one case I was comparing the two closed circuits, the Waters " to and fro " with the circle circuit during anæsthesia. I had made a previous comparison using end-respiratory samples, and found no difference. Various statements have been made from time to time by anæsthetists that there is deficient CO_2 elimination with the Waters circuit but I found *no* difference. I then applied the end-tidal sampler with the infra red analyser and found extremely low values. It is all very well to sample from an Engström respirator where you are getting rid of the whole of each expiration, but when you are removing gases at the rate of half a litre a minute into an infra-red analyser and are using a closed circuit you have to compensate for leakage and maybe you should not sample from a closed circuit with an infra red analyser which is removing gas at $\frac{1}{2}$ litre/min.; and that may explain the very low values. Unfortunately I have not had time to check up on the end-expiratory sample by the Haldane method in closed circuits. The other point was that when I was doing this comparison I suddenly found with the circle circuit that the needle of the Evershed and Vignoles recorder was not coming back to zero. I thought it might be due to kinking in the tubing and so I unkinked the tube; it still did not come back to zero. Then I changed the soda lime and it came back to zero. That was a very obvious change, though I could see nothing abnormal in the patient. We are at the stage when we are just beginning to use it clinically, and I think that there is much more to be learned.

Chairman: It is, of course, possible, and probably desirable, to put the sample back into the circuit after it has been through the analyser. I, for many years, have been using the Brinkman Carbo-visor, which I have fixed on to my machine, and following something which it not, it is true, the end-tidal sample, but something not very far removed from it; and I have found it, as Dr. Nunn suggested, extremely useful for teaching and extremely useful too as a perhaps rather crude indication of end-tidal CO_2. It has never told me that a heart has stopped, but it has told me many other things and it has been quite useful.

XII. THE CLINICAL SIGNIFICANCE OF BLOOD pH AND BLOOD GAS MEASUREMENT

Victor Wynn, M.D.

Surgical Unit, St. Mary's Hospital, Paddington, London, W.2

THE treatment of respiratory failure is a complex problem, as challenging as disorders produced by failure of the heart, kidneys or liver. During the past decade we have come to rely a great deal upon biochemical aids in the elucidation and management of these latter clinical conditions. In the case of disordered respiration assessment has hitherto been based mostly on symptoms, clinical signs and X-rays. Experience gained in the severe poliomyelitis epidemics in recent years, especially in Denmark and Sweden, and in the treatment of large numbers of patients with chronic bronchitis and emphysema in this country, has amply demonstrated the importance of adequate biochemical studies in respiratory failure if the best therapeutic results are to be obtained. We must, I think, regard it as urgent that measurements of blood pH, P_{CO_2} and P_{O_2} be introduced into the routine of clinical biochemistry so that proper tests of ventilatory function may be made. I agree entirely with Griggs et al. (1958) that ventilatory failure is commonly present with many diseases, but is often overlooked because it is difficult to diagnose by symptoms or physical examination. Special problems of diagnosis occur when the patient is breathing an oxygen-enriched mixture, or during anæsthesia, especially during induced hypothermia, and during operations involving the heart or lungs. Interference with the activity of the respiratory centre by drugs or by intracranial lesions provides many clinical examples of respiratory disorder. MacIver et al. (1958) have reported a decrease in the mortality of recent head injuries from 90 per cent to 40 per cent by measures directed towards maintaining adequate ventilation alone. This is a therapeutic result which ranks in importance with the introduction of potassium therapy into the treatment of infantile diarrhœa by Darrow in 1946 and it deserves the widest possible recognition.

The assessment of the ventilatory status does not rest solely with the problem of alveolar hypoventilation and respiratory acidosis. Alveolar hyperventilation leading to respiratory alkalosis is also not uncommon and brings with it a number of untoward physiological changes (Brown, 1953) which are prejudicial to the patient. In my experience there is a real danger that such a patient, who is overbreathing markedly and has a low serum bicarbonate level in consequence, will be diagnosed as suffering from metabolic acidosis and receive treatment for this. Such treatment may aggravate the condition and prove fatal. Alveolar hyperventilation is quite common apart from its usually assigned cause, metabolic acidosis. It occurs in a variety of cerebral disorders, in acute anoxia, cardiac failure, hypotension, hyperpyrexia, salicylate poisoning, water depletion, water intoxication and hepatic failure. Needless to say, patients receiving artificial or assisted respiration are quite as likely to be overventilated as underventilated.

It is unlikely that we would all agree upon the best method of assessing ventilatory status because of our differing requirements and experience.

I think, however, we would be in agreement that the most convenient index of effective alveolar ventilation is the arterial blood P_{CO_2} level. This measurement can be made directly on blood, for example, by bubble equilibration methods, but these are technically difficult. An indirect method is easier, either by measuring the pH and the plasma total CO_2 content, and then utilizing the Henderson-Hasselbalch relationship, or by using the technique of Astrup (1956) which requires an initial pH measurement of the sample, and then two pH measurements after equilibration at known P_{CO_2} levels. A further possibility is the indirect measurement of arterial P_{CO_2} using a rebreathing technique and expired gas analysis (Griggs *et al.*, 1958). This .ethod has inherent advantages but has not yet been fully explored. It would be even more valuable if one could dispense with the rapid infra-red analyser (Campbell and Howell, 1959). This method would still leave unmeasured the blood pH which in itself can provide valuable information. Of the methods discussed above, my preference for general use is the measurement of pH and plasma T_{CO_2}

and the derivation of P_{CO_2} from the Henderson-Hasselbalch equation. This approach adds only one technique (the pH estimation) to routine clinical biochemistry and has the merit of speed and simplicity. Methods of blood pH measurement have been described (see Wynn and Ludbrook, 1957) which are convenient, reproducible and reliable and suitable for routine use.

There remains, however, the problem of arterial puncture, which requires some experience before it is safe. We have attempted to get over this difficulty by using venous blood for pH and P_{CO_2} estimations and have defined the conditions under which it can be successfully employed (Brooks and Wynn, 1959).

The following cases illustrate some of the problems which may be encountered in the management of respiratory failure.

Case I. A somewhat obese plethoric man, aged 44, had a graft inserted into the abdominal aorta because of a thrombosis below the level of the renal arteries to the aortic bifurcation. The operation was carried out under thiopentone—nitrous oxide—oxygen—pethidine—curare anæsthesia with manually controlled respiration and with hypothermia to a rectal temperature of 28° C. The duration of the anæsthetic was about eight hours. The operation was performed uneventfully and the patient was returned to the ward breathing spontaneously and with a normal blood pressure. Re-warming proceeded normally and the patient regained consciousness and spoke rationally about one hour after the end of the operation. Oxygen was administered continuously by means of a plastic face mask and a good colour was maintained.

Three hours postoperatively the patient was noticed by the attendant nurse to be deeply unconscious. As I happened to be in the ward at the time I was summoned urgently and found that the patient appeared to be making no spontaneous respiratory movements, but he was not noticeably cyanosed and his blood pressure, which during the preceding half-an-hour had risen from 140/90 mm. Hg to 200/110 mm. Hg, had dropped suddenly to 115/78 mm. Hg; there was considerable cardiac irregularity. The patient was sweating and his rectal temperature was 34° C. Respiratory arrest was diagnosed and artificial respiration was commenced, at first by hand.

Ten minutes later, an uncuffed endotracheal tube was passed and manually controlled respiration with a free flow of oxygen was commenced. Soon after this procedure started arterial blood was taken for analysis and gave results (Fig. 1) showing that there was a gross respiratory acidosis (pH 6·93, P$_{CO_2}$ 135 mm. Hg) and there was a moderate degree of metabolic acidosis as well.

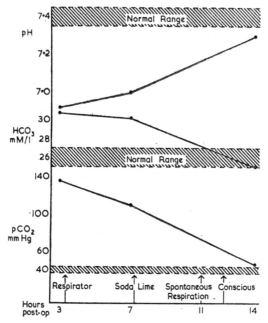

FIG. 1. Case 1. Plasma pH, P$_{CO_2}$ and HCO$_3$ in a patient suffering from postoperative apnœa.

The subsequent course of the patient is of considerable interest. It should be pointed out that this episode occurred several years ago before the problem of postoperative apnœa was properly understood. After 15 minutes of assisted respiration, the patient began to breathe with reasonable respiratory excursions and became conscious. After a further 15 minutes breathing lapsed into its original state of gasping and shallow respirations with long pauses and consciousness was lost (and not regained for nine hours). Assisted respiration was carried

on as described for a further four hours, during which time
the patient's condition gave rise to a great deal of anxiety.
There were no localizing signs of neurological disorder. Plantar
responses were equivocal. There were symmetrical and pur-
poseless movements of both arms and legs and there were head
rolling movements from side to side. Oxygenation seemed to
be normal. A lumbar puncture was performed and a pressure
in excess of 300 mm. of water was observed; the fluid was
clear. At this time the advisability of performing a craniotomy
was seriously considered. I concurred with this view and
thought it would be interesting to repeat the blood pH
estimation and to follow the changes subsequently. When,
however, it was found that despite prolonged artificial ventilation the patient's blood pH had hardly risen from its
previously low level and that the patient's P_{CO_2} was still above
110 mm. Hg, the true diagnosis became obvious; the patient
was still suffering from extreme CO_2 narcosis which had been
unrecognized. Efforts were made to ventilate the patient more
effectively. A cuffed endotracheal tube was passed and a
soda-lime canister was inserted into the circuit; this needed
to be changed approximately every 20 minutes over the subsequent two hours. Three hours later the patient began to
make spontaneous respiratory movements and after a further
hour unassisted respiration began to be well maintained. Soon
after this the patient showed intolerance of the intratracheal
tube, which had to be removed. The patient then regained
consciousness and shortly afterwards seemed to be perfectly
well and rational and showed no untoward effects. Analysis
of the arterial blood showed a return of the pH and P_{CO_2} to
virtually normal levels. The patient's further convalescence
was uneventful.

I think this patient might well have suffered from partial
re-curarization occurring during the re-warming period and
that this led to respiratory inadequacy postoperatively. The
administration of oxygen by means of a plastic face mask may
have aggravated the condition, both by reducing the anoxic
respiratory drive and possibly by reducing the efficiency of
CO_2 elimination by partial rebreathing. At all events, the
life-threatening condition in this patient was severe respiratory
acidosis. Its existence could have been predicted (and was)

at the onset of the respiratory failure and was shown by the initial biochemistry. What was however, unexpected, was its persistence despite what appeared to be adequate efforts at ventilation. I think it cannot be stressed too often that ventilatory insufficiency cannot be excluded with certainty unless a measure of the arterial pH and Pco_2 has been made, and probably these should always be done in any unexplained coma or hypertension. If respiratory acidosis is severe there is a decrease in the force of contraction of the heart, changes in cardiac rate and in coronary blood flow, and these effects can be aggravated by any sudden change in either pH or Pco_2 (McElroy *et al.*, 1958). Moreover, when the pH is low the patient's ability to stand any procedure tending to produce shock (e.g. a small hæmorrhage) is greatly reduced (Hood and Beall, 1958). This has also been my experience.

Case II. A woman of 53 years had several years' history of increasing shortness of breath on exertion and a chronic cough, which was worse in the winter. She had had three

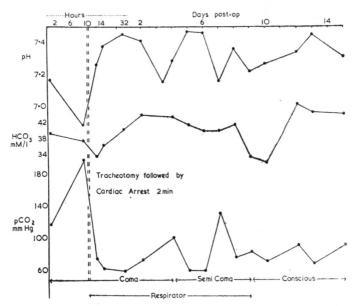

Fig. 2. Case 2. pH, Pco_2 and HCO_3^- in a patient suffering from severe respiratory insufficiency due to bronchitis, emphysema and cor pulmonale.

admissions to hospital over the preceding four years because
of severe bronchitis and emphysema. On the present admission
she was in great respiratory distress and had severe cyanosis.
X-rays of the chest showed the changes of chronic emphysema,
but there was no frank pulmonary consolidation. The patient
was placed in an oxygen tent and although her cyanosis, rest-
lessness and great distress were relieved, the result of this
treatment was that she became deeply unconscious. Initially
the arterial blood showed a severe respiratory acidosis with a
pH of 7·16 and a P_{CO_2} of 116 mm. Hg. While in the oxygen
tent her arterial pH fell to 6·88 and her P_{CO_2} rose to 197 mm. Hg.
A tracheotomy then was performed on the patient. A good
deal of muco-purulent secretion was sucked from the bronchial
tree. Artificial respiration was then commenced by means of
an automatic (Beaver) positive pressure respirator and oxygen
was given as well. Soon after the commencement of artificial
respiration an episode of gross cardiac irregularity occurred,
and for about two minutes no cardiac sounds could be heard
at all. Intravenous restorative drugs were given; the cardiac
beat returned and the blood pressure returned to normal
levels under the influence of noradrenalin. One hour after
artificial ventilation had commenced the arterial blood pH had
risen to 7·26 and the P_{CO_2} had fallen to 74 mm. Hg. (Fig. 2).
A further rise of blood pH and fall of P_{CO_2} occurred during the
next few hours. The patient's condition remained critical,
however, for more than fourteen days. For the first four days
the patient was deeply comatose; for the next six days semi-
comatose, and finally consciousness was regained.

Two and a half years after this episode the patient is still
alive and has been surprisingly well, although she has been
re-admitted to hospital on two occasions for short periods
because of respiratory distress.

I think this case illustrates a number of important clinical
points. In the first place we should now regard the tracheotomy as having been performed far too late, and that the initial
blood sample showing gross alveolar hypoventilation should
have been sufficient indication for the procedure. Of course,
the danger of continuous oxygen administration in under-
ventilating patients is well recognized, but in this case there was
no alternative because of the gross distress of the patient when

not receiving oxygen. Early tracheotomy in many other similar cases has proved most effective in relieving respiratory obstruction, since it enables effective bronchial and tracheal aspiration to be carried out. In this patient bronchial aspiration and artificial respiration very rapidly enabled the respiratory acidosis to be overcome. The very speed with which this was accomplished constitutes, in my opinion, a real threat to the patient. I think it is not unreasonable to attribute the cardio-vascular collapse in this patient, fortunately reversible, to the sudden swing in the pH and P_{CO_2} of the arterial blood. There is ample experimental evidence in both man and dogs that such changes are likely to precipitate severe hypotension, cardiac arrythmia and even ventricular fibrillation and death (Brown and Miller, 1952; Buckley *et al.*, 1953; Dripps, 1947). The practical points are, I believe, that alveolar hypoventilation should not be allowed to proceed to the levels recorded in this patient and that if it occurs efforts at ventilation should be more closely controlled than was the case here. More frequent blood pH analyses would give such control and this is the policy we are pursuing with the management of similar cases at the present time.

Other points of special importance are that the coma of respiratory failure may persist for several days after the relief of anoxæmia and hypercapnœa. It is possible for patients to recover completely from these situations as this patient shows, but it is necessary to establish that the coma is not in fact due to persistent hypercapnœa. In the present case deep coma recurred on the seventh postoperative day although the patient was still receiving artificial respiration and the arterial blood oxygen saturation was normal. Blood analysis showed a recurrence of the respiratory acidosis which was finally attributed to a wrong setting of the respirator. I have seen patients maintained in a coma for several days due to respiratory acidosis because of inadequate ventilation by the respirator. It has always been possible to improve the ventilation by a few simple adjustments of the machine but it is essential to know what the patient's arterial P_{CO_2} level is so that the necessary steps can be taken. Since these patients are usually receiving oxygen, the patient's colour is no guide whatsoever to the state of ventilation.

Case III. A man of 66 had a history of recurrent cough over a period of many years, aggravated during the winter months. For six years he had become increasingly short of breath on exertion and there had been three episodes for which he had been admitted to hospital because of respiratory distress. A diagnosis of chronic bronchitis and emphysema had been made. Prior to the present admission the patient had noticed considerable swelling of both legs. On examination the patient was cyanosed and dyspnœic at rest and had gross pitting œdema of the legs and of the sacrum and increased jugular venous pressure. Examination of the respiratory system showed evidence of bronchitis and emphysema, which was confirmed by X-rays of the chest. The patient also clearly suffered from cardiac failure (cor pulmonale). Arterial blood examination during the first two hospital days showed evidence of a well compensated, mild respiratory acidosis (pH 7·36, P_{CO_2} 76 mm. Hg). The respiratory infection was treated with antibiotics and this infection appeared to improve. The cardiac failure was treated with digitalis and injections of a mercurial diuretic. Under the influence of the diuretics the patient passed very large volumes of urine and his œdema rapidly became less. His clinical condition, however, deteriorated.

I was asked to see the patient on the fifth hospital day because of the occurrence of five major epileptic convulsions which occurred at short intervals, and which left the patient unconscious but without any localizing signs. The analysis of the arterial blood showed that there was now a combined respiratory acidosis and a metabolic alkalosis, the two conditions combining to produce the very high figure of 61 m.moles/l. of plasma bicarbonate. The blood pH was 7·37 and the P_{CO_2} was 108 mm. Hg. It is possible that the convulsions were due to the high P_{CO_2}, since this is known to cause epilepsy as well as unconsciousness, but I suspect that the other metabolic changes which occurred in the patient's blood might well have been contributing factors.

The patient now presented a difficult therapeutic problem, since too effective respiration, with the very high levels of plasma bicarbonate which the patient had, would have been likely to cause a rapid elevation in blood pH, and possibly hypotension and ventricular fibrillation. Tracheotomy was performed, aspiration of the bronchi carried out and for four hours ventilation was performed, using a Beaver positive pressure respirator. At the end of this time the patient's ventilatory insufficiency was unchanged (pH 7·38, Pco₂ 104 mm. Hg) but he was now fully oxygenated, the blood pressure was normal and the heart rate regular (Fig. 3). The respirator was

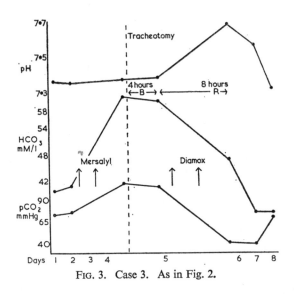

Fig. 3. Case 3. As in Fig. 2.

now changed to the Radcliffe type, which makes provision for negative as well as positive pressure respiration. At the same time the patient was given 500 mg. of acetozolamide (Diamox) intravenously. This produced a spectacular diuresis and the urine contained 178 mEq/l. of bicarbonate. In this way an attempt was made to correct the alkalosis pari-passu with the treatment of the respiratory acidosis. The attempt, however, was only partially successful biochemically speaking, although there were no untoward clinical manifestations. Eight hours after the negative-positive artificial respiration had been started the patient's Pco₂ was normal (41 mm. Hg) but he had a marked metabolic alkalosis (pH 7·68 and bicarbonate 47 m.moles/l.). The artificial respiration was now carried out only intermittently; the metabolic alkalosis was corrected by the further excretion of bicarbonate in the urine and the patient's blood pH and P_{CO_2} returned to the levels observed at the time of admission.

This patient illustrates several metabolic problems in the management of respiratory failure and cor pulmonale. The first is that mercurial diuretics may produce an undesirable metabolic alkalosis because of the excessive loss of H^+ and NH_4^+ ions, which they produce. From an acid-base point of view NH_4^+ ions are equivalent to H^+, and this combined loss is the cause of the metabolic alkalosis seen when the mercurial diuretics are used. A further cause of extracellular alkalosis is the loss of K^+ from the cells, also a common consequence of mercurial diuretics. In this case, however, the cells are made more acid by an ion exchange process, K^+ moving out, and Na^+ and H^+ moving into the cells. Acetozolamide tends to reverse the metabolic alkalosis and consequently it seems logical to use mersalyl alternately with acetozolamide in the management of the œdema associated with respiratory failure. The occurrence of convulsions and unconsciousness draws attention to the serious cerebral disorders which follow alveolar hypoventilation. The effectiveness of the Radcliffe positive-negative pressure respirator in ventilating these patients is clearly shown by the patient's normal P_{CO_2} within eight hours of treatment with this machine having been commenced.

I have chosen these three examples from a larger series of cases which have occurred as routine medical emergencies in a general hospital and which might have occurred anywhere. I am convinced that the proper management of such patients depends, among other things, upon adequate biochemical assistance being available in exactly the same way as one has come to expect it in the case of diabetic coma or uremia.

I would like to outline briefly some of the work which Dr. Brooks and I have done during the past year to see to what extent venous blood could be used for pH and P_{CO_2} measurements in clinical studies. The details of this investigation will be reported elsewhere (*Lancet*, 1959). Briefly, if a patient's hand or arm are heated for 15 minutes with two electrically-heated pads of a common domestic type (Thermega pads), then venous blood drawn without stasis from the back of the

TABLE I. *Arterio-Venous Differences in Plasma pH, T_{CO_2} and P_{CO_2} in Five Groups of Patients (see Legend)*

Group	No. of cases	Skin Temp. °C Mean	Skin Temp. °C Range	Arterio-Venous Differences pH Mean*	pH Range	T_{CO_2} m.moles/l. Mean*	T_{CO_2} Range	P_{CO_2} mm. Hg Mean*	P_{CO_2} Range
A	5	38·2	38·0 – 38·5	0·018 (0·061)	+0·012 (+0·038) to +0·024 (+0·083)	1·3 (2·4)	−0·7 (−1·9) to −2·1 (−3·1)	3·54 (9·6)	−3·0 (−6·3) to −4·8 (−11·4)
B	9	38·4	38·0 – 38·5	0·002 (0·045)	±0·000 (±0·021) to +0·008 (+0·062)	0·4 (1·2)	±0·0 (−0·3) to −0·7 (−2·2)	0·81 (6·7)	±0·0 (−5·5) to −2·1 (−9·1)
C	7	35·2	35·0 – 35·5	0·010 (0·001)	±0·000 (±0·000) to +0·037 (+0·002)	0·2 (0·00)	−0·4 to +0·5	1·2 (0·1)	+0·9 (±0·0) to −2·4 (−0·2)
D	4	34·2 /35·5	34 – 34·5	0·063 (0·003)	+0·024 to +0·073	3·7 (0·3)	−2·2 to −5·0	16·9 (0·1)	−10·8 to −21·2
E	10	35·4	35·0 – 35·5	0·002	±0·000 to +0·009	0·3	−1·1 to +1·0	1·1	−1·1 to +5·0

Group A. The patients were convalescent and were ambulant prior to the test. " Arterialization " of venous blood from the hand was achieved by a period of heating with an electric pad (see text). The skin temperature was taken at the back of the hand at the time of venisection and is highest in Groups A and B because of the local heating. Figures in parenthesis refer to measurements on venous blood obtained simultaneously from the contralateral (unheated) hand.

Group B. Four of the patients were convalescent and five were moderately to severely ill. All were ambulant prior to the tests. " Arterialization " of venous blood was achieved by heating and the figures in parenthesis refer to measurements on venous blood obtained simultaneously from the contralateral (unheated) hand.

Group C. These patients were all severely ill and were confined to bed but had warm extremities. Venous blood was obtained from the back of an unheated hand. The skin temperature was taken at the back of the hand at the time of venisection. Figures in parenthesis refer to blood taken from the contralateral (heated) hand.

Group D. This patient suffered from advanced emphysema and cor pulmonale (see text). Observations were made on the patient on four separate occasions while he was ambulant and a fifth occasion (results are given in parenthesis) when the patient had been confined to bed for one hour. The importance of bed rest is well shown in this patient.

Group E. These patients were operated upon under general anaesthesia. (See Table II.)
T_{CO_2} – Plasma total CO_2 content. P_{CO_2} – Plasma carbon dioxide tension. * Sign disregarded in calculating mean.

hand will have nearly the same pH and P_{CO_2} as arterial blood (Table I, Group A). If the patient is confined to bed before blood is drawn and his whole body surface is therefore warm, the arterio-venous differences, after a period of heating, will be negligible for most clinical purposes (Table I, Group B). Even in seriously ill patients, so long as they are confined to bed and the peripheral circulation is such that the temperature over the dorsum of the hand, as measured by a mercury thermometer in contact with the skin, is at least 35° C., then venous blood drawn without stasis from a hand vein will be sufficiently near arterial blood as far as pH and P_{CO_2} are concerned for most clinical purposes (Table I, Group C). *In such patients heating of the hand is not necessary.* Arterialization of the venous blood has occurred spontaneously in these patients because of their rest in bed and because of the warmth of their body surface promoting peripheral vasodilatation.

A high arterial P_{CO_2} and anoxemia are known to cause peripheral vasodilatation and an increase in peripheral circulation due to a high cardiac output. Spontaneous arterialization of peripheral venous blood can therefore confidently be expected in such patients suffering from alveolar hypoventilation provided that they are not ambulant and that the measured skin temperature over the hand is at least 35° C. (Table I, Group D). This patient's pH was around 7·30, P_{CO_2} 70 to 80 mm. Hg, and oxygen saturation about 80 per cent on the occasions when these tests were made.

General anæsthesia is also associated with spontaneous arterialization of venous blood (Table I, Group E, and Table II). In the ten consecutive cases reported here the agreement between arterial and venous pH, P_{CO_2} and T_{CO_2} levels was remarkably close. The use of venous blood for these measurements during anæsthesia therefore seems to be a decided possibility, thus simplifying the problem for the anæsthetist. Heating the hand is not necessary but a check should be kept on the skin temperature to see that the requisite skin blood flow is being achieved. We have made some observations using blood from the dorsum of the foot and this also seems to be satisfactory, but our cases are few. Our study, however, does not include any patient with a pH greater than 7·44 and P_{CO_2} lower than 34. Respiratory alkalosis is known to cause

TABLE II.   Arterio-Venous Differences in Plasma pH, T_{co_2} and P_{co_2} in Anaesthetized Patients

Case	Anaesthetic	Duration min.	Skin temp. °C	pH A	pH V	pH A—V	T_{co_2} m.moles/l. A	T_{co_2} m.moles/l. V	T_{co_2} m.moles/l. A—V	P_{co_2} mm. Hg A	P_{co_2} mm. Hg V	P_{co_2} mm. Hg A—V
26	P. N₂O, O₂ Rel.	*	n.m.	6·786	6·786	0·000	24·1	24·3	−0·2	137	138	−1·0
27	P. N₂O, O₂ Pet. Rel.	—	n.m.	6·835	6·835	0·000	22·4	21·4	+1·0	116	111	+5·0
		30	35·5	7·163	7·154	+0·009	30·8	30·7	+0·1	81·5	82·6	−1·1
28	P. N₂O, O₂ Rel.	20	35·5	7·252	7·251	+0·001	30·6	30·3	+0·3	66·9	66·5	+0·4
29	P. N₂O, O₂ Rel. Hal.	90	35·5	7·256	7·256	0·000	32·3	32·6	−0·3	70·0	70·7	−0·7
30	P. N₂O, O₂ Pet. Rel.	180	35·5	7·291	7·289	+0·002	26·1	27·2	−1·1	52·5	54·9	−2·4
31	P. N₂O, O₂ Pet. Rel.	30	35·5	7·294	7·294	0·000	29·0	29·5	−0·5	57·9	58·9	−1·0
32	P. N₂O, O₂ Rel. Tr.	75	35·5	7·313	7·310	+0·003	27·6	27·6	0·0	52·9	53·2	−0·3
33	P. N₂O, O₂ Pet. Tel.	30	35·5	7·349	7·349	0·000	29·8	29·9	−0·1	52·8	52·9	−0·1
34	P. N₂O, O₂ Rel. Tr.	30	35·5	7·358	7·358	0·000	27·1	27·3	−0·2	47·1	47·4	−0·3
35	P. N₂O, O₂ Rel. Hal.	120	35·5	7·437	7·437	0·000	23·4	23·4	0·0	34·1	34·1	0·0

Duration — Duration of anaesthetic in minutes at the time of taking blood samples. The venous blood was obtained from an unheated hand. P — Thiopentone. Pet. — Pethidine. Hal. — Halothene. Tr. — Trilene. Rel. — Relaxant.
* The first blood sample was taken at the end of the operation which lasted 2 hours, and the second sample 2 hours later during which time efforts, clearly unavailing, were made to ventilate the patient.
n.m. — Not measured.

TABLE III *Arterio-Venous Differences in Plasma pH, T_{co_2} and P_{co_2} in a Patient with Severe Emphysema, Bronchitis and Cor Pulmonale*

Case	Date 1957	Skin temp. °C	pH		pH A—V	T_{co_2} m.moles/l.		T_{co_2} m.moles/l. A—V	P_{co_2} mm. Hg		P_{co_2} mm. Hg A—V
			A	V		A	V		A	V	
24	7.12	Not measured.	7·374	7·370	+0·004	42·3	42·4	−0·1	71·1	71·8	−0·7
	8.12		7·380	7·363	+0·017	40·5	40·1	+0·4	67·1	68·9	−1·8
	18.12		7·275	7·267	+0·008	40·5	41·5	−1·0	84·4	87·8	−3·4
	20.12		7·302	7·305	−0·003	40·4	40·5	−0·1	79·5	79·1	+0·4
	24.12		7·304	7·306	−0·002	47·9	48·9	−1·0	93·8	95·3	−1·5
	31.12		7·350	7·336	+0·014	49·7	49·9	−0·2	88·1	91·0	−2·9

The venous blood was obtained from the back of an unheated hand.

TABLE IV. *Arterio-Venous Differences in Plasma pH, T$_{CO_2}$ and P$_{CO_2}$ in a Patient with Staphylococcal Pneumonia*

| Case | Date 1958 | Skin temp. °C | pH | | | T$_{CO_2}$ m.moles/l. | | T$_{CO_2}$ m.moles/l. | P$_{CO_2}$ mm. Hg | | P$_{CO_2}$ mm. Hg |
			A	V	A—V	A	V	A—V	A	V	A—V
25	15.4	35	7·473	7·467	+0·006	21·8	22·5	−0·7	29·4	30·8	−1·4
	16.4	35·5	7·390	7·385	+0·005	22·7	23·2	−0·5	36·8	38·0	−1·2
	17.4	35	7·398	7·392	+0·006	23·8	25·5	−1·7	37·9	41·1	−3·2
	22.4	35	7·351	7·351	0·000	23·2	23·8	−0·6	41·0	42·0	−1·0
	2.5	35	7·452	7·436	+0·016	23·5	23·7	−0·2	33·2	34·7	−1·5

The venous blood was obtained from the back of an unheated hand.

peripheral vasoconstriction and consequently this condition might reduce peripheral blood flow. In this case the temperature of the skin would fall.

In Tables III and IV data are presented showing arterio-venous differences in pH, T_{CO_2} and P_{CO_2} levels during the management of two seriously ill patients. The first patient (Table III) suffered from chronic bronchitis, emphysema and cor pulmonale. His illness was very prolonged but ultimately he recovered sufficiently to return home and to resume work. On six occasions the arterio-venous pH and P_{CO_2} differences were negligibly small. The patient's hand did not require heating on any of these occasions nor did we record the skin temperature, since, when this study was done, we had acquired a certain amount of experience at judging when the skin blood flow would be sufficient to ensure arterialization of the venous blood. In the subsequent biochemical management of this patient venous blood alone was employed. Table IV shows the results obtained in a severely ill patient with a staphylococcal pneumonia and alveolar hyperventilation who was studied in the same way as the previous patient. Spontaneous arterialization of the venous blood occurred in this patient despite his critical clinical condition. When this fact was established venous blood alone was used in order to follow the state of his alveolar ventilation.

We believe that the use of venous blood for pH and P_{CO_2} measurements can be a valuable simplification but it must be stressed that the conditions laid down for " induced " (by heating) and "spontaneous" arterialization of the venous blood must be regarded as minimal requirements if grossly misleading values are to be avoided.

I would like to conclude this paper by drawing attention to the fact that a great deal of knowledge about the metabolic aspects of respiratory failure and acid-base disorders was established by physiologists more than 30 years ago. It is now our task to see that, without further delay, this knowledge is applied to the care and treatment of patients.

REFERENCES

ASTRUP, P. (1956). A Simple Electrometric Technique for the Determination of Carbon Dioxide Tensions in Blood and Plasma Total Content of Carbon Dioxide and Plasma, and Bicarbonate Content in " Separated " Plasma at a Fixed Carbon Dioxide Tension (40 mm. Hg). *Scand. J. clin. Lab. Invest.*, **8**, 33.

BROOKS, D., and WYNN, V. (1959). The Use of Venous Blood for pH and CO_2 Studies, especially in Respiratory Failure and during Anæsthesia. *Lancet (to be published).*

BROWN, E. B. Jr. (1953). Physiological Effects of Hyperventilation. *Physiol. Rev.*, **33**, 445.

BROWN, E. B. Jr., and MILLER, F. (1952). Ventricular Fibrillation following a Rapid Fall in Alveolar Carbon Dioxide Concentration. *Amer. J. Physiol.*, **169**, 56.

BUCKLEY, J. J., VAN BERGEN, F. H., DOBKIN, A. B., BROWN, E. B. Jr., MILLER, F. A., and VARCO, R. L. (1953). Postanesthetic Hypotension following Cyclopropane. Its Relationship to Hypercapnia. *Anesthesiology*, **14**, 226.

CAMPBELL, E. J. M., and HOWELL, J. B. L. (1959). The Determination of Mixed Venous and Arterial Blood CO_2 Tension by the Rebreathing Technique. This volume, p. 101.

DARROW, D. C. (1946). Retention of Electrolytes during Recovery from Severe Dehydration due to Diarrhœa. *J. Pediat.*, **28**, 515.

DRIPPS, R. D. (1947). Immediate Decrease in Blood Pressure seen at the Conclusion of Cyclopropane Anæsthesia, " Cyclopropane Shock." *Anesthesiology*, **8**, 15.

GRIGGS, D. E., HACKNEY, J. D., COLLIER, C. R., and AFFELDT, J. E. (1958). The Rapid Diagnosis of Ventilatory Failure with the CO_2 Analyser. *Amer. J. Med.*, **25**, 31.

HOOD, R. M., and BEALL, A. C. Jr. (1958). Hypoventilation, Hypoxia and Acidosis occurring in the Acute Postoperative Period. *J. Thorac. Surg.*, **36**, 729.

McELROY, W. R. Jr., GERDES, A. J., and BROWN, E. B. Jr. (1958). Effects of CO_2, Bicarbonate and pH on the performance of Isolated Perfused Guinea Pig Hearts. *Amer. J. Physiol.*, **195**, 412.

MacIVER, I. N., FREW, I. V., and MATHESON, J. G. (1958). The Role of Respiratory Insufficiency in the Mortality of Severe Head Injuries. *Lancet*, **i**, 390.

WYNN, V., and LUDBROOK, J. (1957). A Method for Measuring the pH of Body Fluids. *Lancet*, **i**, 1068.

DISCUSSION

Chairman: Thank you, Dr. Wynn, for that interesting paper and for bringing us down to earth. One point I am not quite sure about is that you said that you cannot effectively ventilate a patient with no blood pressure. I was under the impression that I had done so on several occasions. Would you like to elaborate on that?

Wynn: I am only taking the attitude that it would be difficult to ventilate a patient. In the patient who had a pH of 6·7 we did everything we could to ventilate him and we failed. I have seen this before and I just assumed we failed because we were not getting blood through the lungs in sufficiently large quantities, but that may be wrong.

Campbell: If, in fact, your circulation is in abeyance, of course. Whereas you can move the air in and out of the lungs all right, you will not be doing anything to alter the state of the tissues, and where the critical level of low blood flow is at which this appears I would not like to say. I have often wondered about it. It must be a very small blood flow indeed, I think.

Chairman: I think we must be careful not to equate in our minds blood pressure as recorded by the sphygmomanometer in circumstances which are often far from ideal with the blood flow through the lungs.

Severinghaus: I wonder if Dr. Wynn would elaborate on the opening statement that overventilation is very serious and often results in death. I do not know anything about this syndrome.

Wynn: Clinically, of course, the average student is taught that overventilation is commonly due to acidosis. Every textbook of medicine teaches you that the way you recognize acidosis is by hyperventilation and the way you recognize alkalosis is by underventilation. I was recently asked to review a book in which things were round the other way. I think that must have been an error. But in actual fact neither of those statements is true. Acidosis producing a doubling or a trebling of alveolar ventilation is clinically compatible with a type of respiratory excursion which the average clinician would not recognize as overbreathing. That is to say, you can move air in and out of the alveoli two or three times more than normally without a clinician being able to say that this is in fact happening, and yet gross overbreathing is said to be a sign of acidosis. What happens in acidosis to cause gross overbreathing is usually some complication and the complications which are commonly the cause of overbreathing are cardiac complications, cardiac failure, pulmonary complications—pneumonia—or hæmatological complications like blood loss and anæmia, or something like this. If I were asked to list the order of conditions in which I see, or am asked to see, patients who are obviously overbreathing, then I would put acidosis somewhere in the middle of that list. I think that the list would be headed by cerebral disease of some sort, some sort of intracranial complication whether it be hæmorrhage, thrombosis or infection, and probably infection would be very high on that list. These patients are overbreathing, they have low P_{CO_2}'s. I think probably next, in ordinary clinical cases, I would put some problem of water, either depletion (certainly that would be the common one) or water intoxication which has to be acute and severe to give overbreathing. Now, water depletion, I think is a very common cause of overbreathing. I think it is the cause of overbreathing in most diabetics who overbreathe after the correction of the acidosis. I do not think that overbreathing of diabetic acidosis is due to acidosis alone. That is the first point, and the second point is that I believe its continuation may be due to intracellular water depletion. Now another group are the hepatic failures, but hepatic failure, I think, is the least common group. Then there is the acidotic group. You will notice that I have not mentioned cardiac failure at all so far. I think that is rather complicated and that you really do need to know P_{CO_2}'s very accurately to know what the cause of overbreathing is in cardiac failure. Now let us take this group (2) and group (3) as simple cases of overbreathing. That is to say, patients who are breathing perhaps maximally and have P_{CO_2}'s in the region of 15 to 20 millimetres of mercury. Among this group (2) I think the mortality is very high. I think the mortality is high because of complications, which are mostly metabolic—I think Ramwell mentioned this— they are difficult to keep in ordinary water and electrolyte balance, they tend to lose sodium, of course. You will find the physiology of overventilation described by Brown in Physiological Reviews (1953). I would not be surprised if it was very close to your own paper an anæsthesia. Didn't you write one with Dripps on anæsthesia?

Severinghaus: In the *Physiological Review*.

Wynn: I think, if you look up the *Physiological Review* your own paper will be followed by one by Brown on Hyperventilation and its physiological effects. I have never seen an account of hyperventilation and its *clinical* effects. All I can say is that patients who are hyperventilating for a long time are inclined not to recover for that reason alone. And, of course, in the hepatic failures, who have only been recognized in the last few years as suffering from overventilation, there has been an attempt to give these people CO_2 to breathe, and Randall's group, for example, in America regard the respiratory alkalosis as a significant lesion and as a possible cause of death in hepatic failure. We have given patients with hepatic failure CO_2 to breathe in order to treat the hyperventilation. We have never had any success with it.

Chairman: Thank you, Dr. Wynn. You mention overbreathing as a common cause of death, but the examples you have given us are of overbreathing as secondary; and I as an anæsthetist am bound to think of overbreathing not resulting from a compensatory process in a patient but imposed on a patient by an anæsthetist; and as I know well, now we have started taking measurements, it is very easy for an anæsthetist to overbreathe for a patient. This happens commonly, but I think it is very rare for it to be followed by disaster or even by any serious consequences. Perhaps Dr. Astrup could answer that question.

Astrup: Yes. I can say that during the polio epidemic in Copenhagen in 1952 we had over 100 patients at least who were ventilated and they were all overventilated for weeks—some for months—and their P_{CO_2}'s were between 20 and 25. And we did not see any bad effects from this long term overventilation. As far as I know the only thing which can happen is the formation of renal stones.

Geddes: I am very interested in Dr. Wynn's use of venous blood for sampling. We in Liverpool have been following hyperventilation under light nitrous oxide relaxant anæsthesia. We have eliminated the use of pentothal which gives an alteration on the

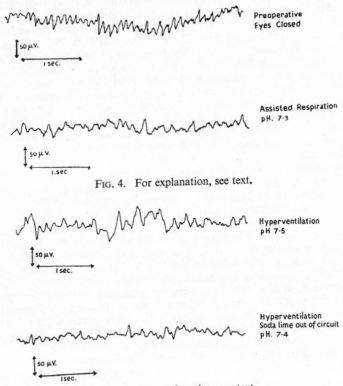

Preoperative
Eyes Closed

50 μV.

1 sec.

Assisted Respiration
pH. 7·3

50 μV.

1.sec

FIG. 4. For explanation, see text.

Hyperventilation
pH 7·5

50 μV.

1 sec.

Hyperventilation
Soda lime out of circuit
pH. 7·4

50 μV.

1sec.

FIG. 5. For explanation, see text.

E.E.G. which we have used to monitor the effects of hyperventilation. Actually, one of the things that happens with hyperventilation is a decrease in blood flow in the periphery and we have in actual fact warmed the patient's hands prior to taking the blood samples. We have not got anything as nice and neat as your electric pad, I think that is a very good idea. If I may, I should like to show a couple of slides of the E.E.G. at different pH's. Blood was obtained by venous sampling. I notice, incidentally, from Table II in Dr. Wynn's paper of pH during anæsthesia, that all the pH's

DISCUSSION 187

were on the acid side. The first tracing (Fig. 4) is with the patient conscious, eyes closed—for a normal E.E.G. The second tracing was with assisted respiration on top circuit, following intubation with scoline. The pH was 7·3. Here (Fig. 5), by hyperventilation, we have altered the pH to 7·5, and large slow wave activity has appeared. The last tracing is with the patient being hyperventilated with the soda lime out of circuit, and this large slow wave activity has disappeared with a pH of 7·4.

Scurr: We are occasionally told by other clinicians that we attach too much importance to CO_2 levels, and I would like to know at what level of P_{CO_2} and pH things become dangerous and coma is likely to supervene. In my own experience it is round about a P_{CO_2} of 80. I wonder if Dr. Wynn has any information on that.

Wynn: Yes. I think that is correct. But of course the situation is difficult. pH itself has an effect in the situation. The lower the pH I think the more susceptible a patient is to the effects of a high P_{CO_2}. If you have any clinicians who feel that you are paying too much attention to these things, I think one ought to remind them about the situation when electrolytes started to be estimated. Sodium estimations started to be performed by easy methods about eight years ago, or a little before, in most places. Most clinicians were happy with the old situation, and asked for, in an ordinary hospital, let us say, 200–300 sodium estimations per year. At St. Mary's Hospital for sodium alone we are now doing between 4,000 and 5,000 per year, and Dr. Astrup is doing 30,000 per year. This is correct, isn't it?

Astrup: Yes, it is.

Wynn: Now, you see, all of us who have been interested in electrolytes have been through this battle once before, we know we are going to go through it again, and we know that we must win. I had these conversations eight years ago: (a) flame photometers are not necessary because you have chemical techniques; (b) plasma sodiums are not necessary, all you want is clinical judgement; (c) milliequivalents, whoever wants them? Why not stick to milligrammes per cent? But who is seriously going to advocate the old terminology of milligrammes per cent to-day? Who would say that plasma sodiums are not necessary? Such a person would belong to an entirely out-of-date generation. And the clinicians of to-day must be confronted with the fact that they must have measurements, and the measurements that we have been discussing in the last two days are the measurements they must have. And certainly whether we pay too much attention to them at this stage, whether we exaggerate them, whether we overemphasize them at this stage, it will all be ironed out in the future. But at this point we have got to press for them.

Chairman: Thank you, Dr. Wynn. I will ask Dr. Campbell to be the final speaker in this discussion.

Campbell: I think the point I was going to say, Dr. Astrup, is that your cases are highly selected in that they live. Your patients were alive, and therefore they were selected. I would be much more interested to know of patients in whom, shall we say, respiratory alkalosis is acutely produced in some conditions and that they should die. This sort of information is much more difficult to come by. From the effects that Haldane demonstrated back in 1915 we know that nasty things happen to the vasomotor centre. From the E.E.G. record, such as you have been producing, we know that nasty things happen to the brain and so on. It is going to be very difficult to decide whether, in fact, respiratory alkalosis by itself ever causes death. But I do not think that exonerates us from paying attention to the fact that it may become a contributory factor. My concern with this was brought up by a case of salicylate intoxication in which the P_{CO_2} was very low, and I know of two patients who died while being given sodium bicarbonate as treatment for salicylate poisoning.

REFERENCE

BROWN, E. B. (1953). Physiological effects of hyperventilation. *Physiol. Rev.* **33**, 445.

XIII. FINAL GENERAL DISCUSSION

Chairman: As one of the people responsible for bringing together on these two days a galaxy of talent which includes physicists, physical chemists, chemical physicists, chemical pathologists, clinical physiologists, physicians, surgeons and anæsthetists, I had a haunting fear that we might meet and have, as we have had, a full and interesting discussion, but that we might all go away from it with nothing settled. Whether that fear is to be realized or not will perhaps become apparent during the next half hour. I feel it would be a great thing if out of this Conference could come some very definite measure of agreement from us; some points on which clinicians might even take action; some firm recommendations. It is important, however, that we should not for the sake of apparent agreement discard any of the principles to which we would like to hold. I want to start the discussion on a clinical level and I am going to ask Mr. Hobsley, as a clinician who sees many sides of the problem, to put his ideas about the way in which metabolic disturbances can be, and should be, presented to the clinician.

Hobsley: When Dr. Woolmer asked me to start the ball rolling in this discussion, I was absolutely flabbergasted, to use an old-fashioned word, because in this distinguished company I am only too conscious of my own lack of distinction. I have only been in this field for about a year. On the other hand I think possibly Dr. Woolmer chose very well for a reason which I will come to in just one moment. You see, what we are going to try to decide is a problem in education. We are trying to impart our ideas to other people who are not familiar with them. It always seems to me that in a problem of communication—of putting ideas over to other people—you have first to decide that you have something that is worth putting over. Now, I for one, if I was not convinced before, would certainly be convinced by Dr. Wynn's paper, even without the other contributions, that we have something worth putting over to the clinicians. But the second thing to decide is who you are going to put it over to. I feel we must put it over to the clinician who is an intelligent person, but without perhaps the scientific training and the training in these aspects of biology with which we are particularly concerned here. And that is why I think that Dr. Woolmer was right to choose me because I am the nearest one among you to this abstract person. I have only been involved in these measurements and estimations of various types for nine months and I can still remember my horror when I met the pH/ bicarbonate diagram, and then later on my horror when I realized that there were other kinds of diagram, such as Dr. Astrup would like us to use, and so on. I can remember this all too clearly and perhaps a little more vividly than some of you can do. And then the final thing in an educational project like this is that you have to decide to what level you are going to raise the standards of people at whom you are directing your education. That raises a problem which I will mention again in a few moments' time. But I know that the clinicians have tremendous psychological blocks to an interpretation of acid-base problems which involves either charts or logarithms. I think there is really no question about that at all. The clinician will want to know whether his patient's blood is more acid or more alkaline than normal. You have to quantitate things, of course, so I think that you ought to tell him what the pH is; you ought to educate him to know that when the pH goes up the blood becomes more alkaline and vice versa. Sometimes you still have to do that. You tell him what the pH is, you give him in brackets the normal range and you say: " This blood is more alkaline," or " less alkaline " than usual. I think I would prefer to use the term " acidæmia " or " alkalæmia " rather than acidosis or alkalosis so as to avoid any conceptual difficulties when it comes to a respiratory alkalosis, plus a metabolic acidosis, perhaps giving rise to an acidæmia or an alkalæmia, depending which component is greater. You then want to give him some idea of the two components which are making up together the actual pH of the blood. In other words, I think you must tell him the partial pressure of carbon dioxide in the blood—and again you have to put in the normal value of 40 millimetres of mercury and say that this is above normal or below normal—and you have to educate him that if it is above normal the patient is not breathing adequately and that if it is below normal the patient is breathing over-adequately. Some clinicians still have to be slightly educated along those lines. but at least it's keeping it as simple as it can possibly be kept. And then finally you have to bring in this metabolic component of it. I did suggest earlier that we could express this as a bicarbonate excess or deficit compared with what one would have expected at the P_{CO_2} one actually has. That may not be the best way of expressing it. It may be better to say that at this P_{CO_2} we would have normally expected a blood pH of such and such—in fact the blood is more acid than that or the blood is more alkaline than that and this is the metabolic component. But then we come to the last bit—to what level do we expect to be able to educate the clinician in the first instance? And this I think is really the vital point—that if we are going to educate the clinician to recognize these factors it is going to be too much to expect him at first to be able necessarily to cope with them himself. And if you are going to give him this very well worthwhile information I think it is important that you should also be able to tell him at the same time that there is somebody, some specialist in these things who understands these things very well, who will be only too pleased to assist him to cope with any problems that have arisen as a result of the

determinations that he has asked for. No doubt he will not take
advantage of those specialist investigators, perhaps even most of
the time, but I think it very important that he should know that
they are there to fall back on in a last resort if he really feels that
he would not like to undertake the treatment himself. In other
words, that there should be acid-base teams or departments available
as a nucleus of really extremely specialized information. I would like
to rest my case there, Sir.

Chairman: Thank you very much, Mr. Hobsley. It was a very
clear presentation.

Payne: I think Dr. Wynn has drawn attention to an aspect of
clinical anæsthesia which probably deserves considerably more
attention than it has had. In this ageing population it is not uncommon to find patients who are in a very advanced state of
metabolic acidosis before they even reach the operating table and
as anæsthetists we compensate for that acidosis fairly effectively
by overventilation and we then transfer the patient at the end of
the operation to the post-operative ward if we are fortunate enough
to possess one. Otherwise the patient goes back to an ordinary
ward. What happens then is anyone's guess. I do not think I
am being unfair to my clinical colleagues when I say that the
average approach to the post-operative period is to look at such a
patient and to say: " Ah, yes. She is breathing well," and to
drift away satisfied. In fact, if the anæsthetist cared to measure
the P_{CO_2} of such a patient he might find it in the region of 20
millimetres of mercury. If he took the trouble to measure the
oxygen consumption he might find it somewhere around 500 ml.,
especially if the temperature was raised, and if he went further and
measured the minute volume it might be anything between 10 and
15 litres. This is the sort of minute volume and oxygen consumption required by a coalman when he carries 1 cwt. of coal up two
flights of stairs in a pair of army boots. And we expect these
elderly patients who have undergone major operations to continue
to survive under these circumstances! The miracle really is that
such patients survive the length of time they do. And when they
die, of course we console ourselves with the fact that: " Well, she
was a pretty poor risk anyway." The point I am making is this,
unless we take the trouble to make the measurements that Dr.
Wynn and Dr. Astrup have pretty well forced upon us to-day, we
do not know really whether the patient's " adequate " ventilation
is in compensation for her metabolic acidosis or whether she is
really well, and unless we have this information we cannot effectively
undertake her post-operative management, and I have no doubt
in my own mind that the sooner we accept the lessons of to-day the
better it will be for our patients.

I have been fortunate in the last few months to collaborate with
Dr. Holmdahl in Uppsala in some investigations of halothane
anæsthesia using Dr. Astrup's methods, and it was a striking

feature of these patients that although there was some degree of respiratory acidosis associated with the anæsthesia, there was no evidence of *metabolic* acidosis except in patients who had previously shown that evidence, or who had developed hypoxia for some reason during the course of the operation. These patients invariably had a metabolic acidosis in the post-operative period and I am not sure that we have ever really appreciated these distinctions before. It is for this reason that I support very strongly what Dr. Wynn and Mr. Hobsley have had to say this afternoon.

Chairman: Thank you, Dr. Payne. Of course, in the old days when open ether was the common anæsthetic and we used large quantities of it and, indeed, in the days which not many of you will remember when we used chloroform quite commonly, we were dimly aware that we were inducing in our patients a metabolic acidosis. I don't think this worried us very much. Perhaps it did not worry us as much as it worried our patients. I think most anæsthetists to-day have the impression that with modern agents we, the anæsthetists at any rate, are not to blame for a metabolic acidosis. I am not entirely happy, however, that that is so. I am not sure that we can get off as lightly as this. Professor Pask, I know, has given this a good deal of thought. Have you anything to say just now, Professor Pask?

Pask: Nothing on that, Sir, but I have one or two odd points on which I would like further enlightment if I may raise them. First of all, in Dr. Ramwell's presentation he said that what I think he called the intermittent sample end-tidal air on the whole gave greater agreement with arterial P_{co_2} than continuous sampling with measurement of the end plateau. I take it that what was happening was that in intermittent sampling only the ends of the plateau were being put through the instrument and none of the other air. Was the better agreement, I wonder, simply due to an instrumental defect and the engine was never being ventilated with air that was far from the stuff he was trying to estimate? I imagine that was the explanation, but I wonder if I am correct.

Ramwell: The work was that of Collier, Affeldt and Farr who obtained better agreement with arterial blood by using continuous fractional sampling rather than continuous sampling of all the expiration. They used the Liston-Becker model 16. I think their results reflected the limitations of the instrument.

Pask: Pursuant to that, I may perhaps give a grain of at least companionship, if not of comfort, to Dr. Ramwell because we still do, in specific instances, make considerable use of end-tidal sampling. That is in patients (I must admit whether or not they have pathology of the lungs), who are on continuous artificial respiration, and where the respiratory frequency is low, and where the sample is taken at the extreme end of the expiratory period, and where it is passed repeatedly through a buffered indicator so that the result is not influenced by breath to breath variations. In other words, an averaged and stale estimate of end-tidal P_{CO_2}. Now, this is valuable because you can see what is changing as soon as you go into the room and if you see that it has changed and the change bears any relationship to the other clinical evidence this is a strong reason for doing a Plesch sample, which we then do and estimate with the same technique of estimation. Dr. Wynn's presentation naturally interested me a great deal. I think one thing that bothers one as a clinician is not what *can* happen but what is very likely to happen, and I was a little surprised by his second slide (Fig. 2, p. 171). It showed what I believe was an emphysematous patient who had cardiac arrest. I am surprised that he was indeed able to ventilate that patient so vigorously that he could produce that rapid fall in blood acidity. I should have thought that it was an unusual patient in whom one could, however hard one tried to ventilate, produce such a catastrophic change that the heart stopped. Coming back to the anæsthetist's question which really is: if I am going to ventilate a patient artificially over a period of, let us say, six hours, supposing I do it generously what sort of debt in terms of carbon dioxide are we likely to set up? I think this would be a useful way of expressing it. Because if the debt of CO_2 is only going to be of the order of 2 or 3 minutes apnœa in order to be recovered it would not be so seriously worrying to us. If, on the other hand, it is going to require a very much longer and more drastic period of correction it would be very concerning. I think it is clear enough that if you do not let any CO_2 come out it must accumulate at a fairly rapid rate, but I am not clear how grave a debt we would be likely to produce in, say, six hours overventilation. I should think 20 litres a minute is the maximum we are ever likely to achieve under anæsthetic circumstances.

Harbord: There seem to be several different kinds of respiratory difficulty. For example, some patients have laboured chest movements suggestive of high respiratory flows, whereas when a bag is connected, very little air enters it. I think this aspect requires more study.

Lucas: The only point I would like to make after listening for two days is that I think we are all in agreement that we must make measurements of pH in metabolic acidosis and alkalosis, and we must make them and present them to the clinicians so that they can understand them. But the clinician has one great objection to, shall we say, the applied physiologist in the ward—this is traditional for him—that he feels that the man who is going to come and make measurements of this sort is going to do it come what may concerning the patient. The investigation I am thinking of particularly is arterial puncture. Those of us who have done it and have had it done on ourselves feel it is a justifiable thing to do, but the average clinician views with extreme horror that anybody should want to go and puncture an artery except inadvertently. I think that is a very cogent reason for moving over to using venous blood, even though the accuracy of it may not be so great. The clinicians *per se* are not greatly interested in the third decimal place or even the second, or sometimes even the first, but it is quite fair game for anybody to take venous blood off a patient. So if we could agree that for purposes of clinical investigation venous sampling or capillary sampling could be adopted as standard, then I think we would go a long way towards getting the clinician to agree with us, but there is this tendency: " Oh, you chaps from the laboratory, you just come in and do things to our patients that we have to explain to them when their arm drops off."

Chairman: Thank you, Dr. Lucas. I must say, I am rather taken with the suggestion that one can use capillary blood. That, I suppose, might solve quite a number of difficulties. If we could be reasonably sure, as I think from what Dr. Astrup has told us we can, that capillary blood is (provided certain elementary precautions are taken) a reliable indication of arterial blood. Would you agree with that, Dr. Astrup?

Astrup: I have not actually myself compared the results for P_{CO_2}. For standard bicarbonate it is the same.

Severinghaus: Capillary blood, in other people's hands, will lead to problems which you may not get in your own hands; two at least. One is that it may be quite difficult to assure that they do have an anaerobic transfer from the capillary to the micro pH electrode, and the other is a problem of squeezing tissue fluids out with the blood. The people who have measured finger drop samples have often said that there is hæmo-dilution due to tissue fluid as compared with a venous sample, and that would presumably lower the standard bicarbonate if people do have to squeeze to get the blood out.

Chairman: I suppose another objection to the use of venous blood is that venous blood is not homogenous; it is not the same everywhere in the body. This, I suppose, applies too to arterial blood but not with anything like the same force. If you take venous blood from the antecubital fossa, however careful you are about anaerobic precautions and all the rest of it, I have a feeling that this may not be representative of the central venous blood.

Lucas: Perhaps we might, by being so accurate, be defeating our own ends. At the minute we are trying to convince the clinician that he needs pH measurements in everyday medicine and the cases that Dr. Wynn has cited—and I am sure a lot of us in this room could cite other cases of metabolic disturbances which have not been spotted by the clinician—that even if our pH measurements are not strictly comparable because the venous samples have been taken from both arm and leg at different times at least we could give the clinician some idea of what was going on in the body. I think if we started off by just taking measurements which were fairly gross knowing full well in our minds that they were gross and they would be no use for investigational purposes, but for therapeutic reasons they would be of value.

Chairman: Yes, of course, I would happily accept that idea if we were sure that the error was not going to be so big as to lead us to give the clinician wrong advice. If, however, it was and you said of a venous sample: " Oh, this patient has got so and so and you must do such and such," and the patient gets worse instead of better, and this because we have taken a venous instead of an arterial sample for instance, then the method is only further discredited and we shall do ourselves more harm than good. It may well be though, as I take it you suggest, that the error we arrive at from using a venous sample instead of an arterial is not likely to result in that.

Lucas: I do not think it would, if we presuppose that those people who are going to take it are skilled enough in their technique to be able to do arterial bloods for investigational purposes, surely the error in their method of taking venous blood will not approach the error of not knowing whether it is 7·6 or 6·9?

Pask: There is great appeal in Dr. Wynn's suggestion of using arterialized venous blood, which I think presupposes that the blood is obtained predominantly from the skin, where in the normal way you can get rapid flow without much increase in metabolism. The practical snag is by the time the patient is very far up the creek the hands are liable to be gelatinous masses of hæmatomata because of repeated punctures. I think Dr. Wynn would be doing us a great service if he can find out whether you can do the same thing on the foot as well, because you will probably need all the available veins.

Wynn: You can do it on the foot, but I would rather stick to hands.

Nunn: I don't think it is out of place to stress that there are big differences in the composition of blood from different veins. Veins on the back of the hand contain predominantly blood from the fingers and under suitable conditions it is known to approximate closely to arterial blood. But the blood from the antecubital fossa is primarily draining muscles. I cannot give figures for saturation but it is clearly very desaturated. In our experience the pH is about 7·3, and on occasions it has been down to 7·2. I believe that the mean P_{co_2} is about 52 mm. Hg compared with 40 Hg for arterial blood.

Brooks: I think it depends very much on how the blood is taken, that is why I would probably personally be against a technician taking blood from the antecubital fossa with stasis for pH estimation. But as long as certain conditions are fulfilled, such as the skin temperature and the fact that one has not used stasis and the patient is at rest and warm then a close approximation, or an identity, with arterial blood can be obtained.

Nunn: But surely the site of puncture is the most important parameter.

Brooks: Oh, the back of the hand. I am sorry, I should have said that.

Chairman: Is Dr. Campbell registering complete disagreement with this?

Campbell: No, I am not registering disagreement. I am just thinking that although you have tied this all up very carefully *here* with these conditions, in fact your conditions will gradually get looser and looser by passing from hand to hand and mouth to mouth and in the end people will just say: " Oh, some chap has just shown that venous blood is as good as arterial blood," and secondly, I personally just do not know what all the fuss about arterial puncture is. I have never had any trouble with it. In many cases where I have been to see patients to take blood samples, the houseman has said, " We are having great difficulty getting blood from this patient for hæmoglobin. Would you let us have some of the blood you get from the artery because we cannot get into the veins." I think that if you cannot do arterial punctures for any reason, provided you use these criteria your method is all right, but I think it is probably more important to go round hospitals doing arterial punctures showing people that they are not dangerous or uncomfortable.

Chairman: I think that few of us have the skill which Dr. Campbell either has naturally or has technically acquired. I know my own attempts at arterial puncture were by no means uniformly successful.

Wynn: It is obviously going to be impossible to prevent people taking the data that Dr. Brooks and I have put together on the use of venous blood, and misusing those data. For example, they will be in great difficulties if they take the venous blood from the wrong site and under the wrong conditions. To prevent this education and example are going to be necessary as they are in the rest of blood pH work. I would now like to refer to two subjects mentioned by Professor Pask. First of all, the patient he referred to on my slide 2 (p. 171), with the very rapid ventilatory response to artificial respiration, did have a short period of cardiac arrest, but this is an incident which lasted only a few minutes in a total period of over 45 minutes. It was overcome quickly, although it was very frightening at the time, and I would personally prefer to avoid it. That patient did, in fact, ventilate very quickly. I also made a strong point about patients with low blood pressure being difficult to ventilate and that sometimes their low blood pressure was due to respiratory acidosis or, at any rate, a very low pH. The second point is that if you have an ill patient who is being anæsthetized, provided the skin temperature reaches 35° C., he has not got vasoconstriction and the venous pH at the back of his hand will be near to his arterial pH. If he has gross disturbance of blood pH, for example, suppose it is near 7·0, then a small arterio-venous difference at this level is of no clinical importance and the information available to the anæsthetist whether to ventilate more or less is reliable.

Geddes: Recently, at another meeting I had the opportunity of hearing Dr. Campbell give a description of his technique for arterial puncture. I think it would be a good idea if it was put on the record at this meeting.

Campbell: Well, these are the precautions I observe. If it is to be an isolated puncture there must be pressure over the site of the puncture for five minutes afterwards sufficient to obliterate the pulse below it. You then release the pressure and watch the site carefully for a minute. If you do not see anything happening you just go away. If you see any sign of a swelling appearing or anything like that you press again for five minutes. Having had an indwelling needle in you wait for ten minutes, and with these precautions I have not had difficulty at any time, with one exception; a lady who had an indwelling arterial needle in and who became violent and started beating me over the head with a needle in her arm. She did get a hæmatoma at the site which caused a little temporary weakness. I think to hold that against arterial puncture is like holding it against lumber puncture when a man gets off the bed and starts walking away with the needle in his back—it is not really fair to the technique. But I think this pressure afterwards is very important, and I would take anybody to any arterial puncture I have done at any time within minutes afterwards and ask them to ask the patient: " Was it uncomfortable, or did you feel it?" however often you like. After he has had it he will say: " No trouble whatsoever." I think you have just got to go round doing it. I used to meet opposition: " You can't go sticking needles into my patients' arteries," and now at the hospital I am called when people cannot get *venous* blood!

Chairman: That puts you in a strong position.

Ramwell: I think the great objection to arterial puncture is that it is a technique which cannot be widely practised by technicians and we want arterial blood to be taken routinely. A lot of work has been done on this and I have always been impressed by the amount of blood you can get out of an ear which has had a 40 watt bulb shone on it. You take a piece of glass capillary, put it into the lobe and it pulls out a plug of tissue and you get a very profuse flow of blood—ample for even the most elaborate pH methods and this blood is equivalent to arterial.

Chairman: Mr. Hobsley suggested that you must not frighten clinicians by logarithms or diagrams and the innuendo has been made—I have been partly responsible for it myself—that clinicians are simple-minded people. Well, I like to regard myself as a clinician and I would like it to go on record that I am even more simple-minded than the most simple-minded clinician, but I do not object to diagrams; at least, some diagrams I do not object to, and I would put in a plea for the pH bicarbonate diagram—the Davenport diagram—which is a thing that even I can understand and which has a delightfully simple logic attached to it. From where the spot is on this diagram you can in a moment arrive at a complete analysis of the acid-base state of the patient's blood. This seems to be a method of presentation which has considerable appeal, and which can appeal logically to the clinician, and I would like to know why we cannot suggest that this be the method of presentation.

Nunn: I can see no reason why it should not be. Although I would not like to say why I should prefer a Davenport diagram to a $pH/\log P_{CO_2}$ plot. To my way of thinking the information to be derived from the two are pretty much the same, The special advantage of the pH/bicarbonate diagram is that the P_{CO_2} can be read off directly. Also, one can show serial changes on the diagram. If a pH/bicarbonate comes back from the lab. with the first readings plotted, then subsequent readings can be added and it may be possible to show the patient going through a cycle, coming back to the original point. This has been done by a number of anæsthetists in describing acid-base upsets and I myself find it very easy to follow. Dr. Campbell, I know, has put this diagram over to undergraduates—in fact, at the Middlesex Hospital they carry them round in their waistcoat pockets.

Wynn: There is one serious defect in this diagram and that is that it only covers about one half or one third of the clinical range and the top of your P_{CO_2} isobar is 80. The top cases that I have got are 190.

Nunn: That is being rectified. In fact it is on the drawing board of our department at the moment.

Hobsley: If I may say something here, Sir, I also, like Dr. Campbell and possibly because of Dr. Campbell, use the pH/ bicarbonate diagram to express my own results and I find it very useful and very valuable and very easy. With regard to the difference between the pH/bicarbonate diagram and the $pH/\log P_{CO_2}$ diagram, I do not think there is any. They are surely just two different ways of graphically representing the same basic equation. They are just treating your recordings differently. The only advantage, I think, that the pH/bicarbonate diagram has when it comes to this question of education, if you are going to have the diagram at all, is that that y axis is just simple bicarbonate in milliequivalents per litre which the clinician understands perfectly well, as distinct from the logarithm of the P_{CO_2}. I have no doubt that it is important to avoid logarithms. In any case, I do not think that the pH/ bicarbonate diagram—I differ from Dr. Nunn here—is necessary for the understanding of a report on a patient provided that it includes those three points that I mentioned: that their blood pH is such and such (normal such and such), i.e. acidæmia or alkalæmia; and the P_{CO_2} is such and such (normal such and such), i.e. the patient is overbreathing or underbreathing; and the third one I find a little difficult, but it could be either expressed as a bicarbonate excess or deficit compared to what one would have expected at the given P_{CO_2}, or it could be expressed as a difference in pH from what was actually found. I do not think it is necessary to have the diagram and I do know from personal experience that when you confront people for the first time with that diagram there is a very great psychological block to attempting to understand it.

Ludbrook: I would like to place myself on record as an anti-diagram man too. I agree with the remark about this diagram that it has too many curls in it. At the moment we present the results of plasma sodium, potassium, chloride etc. estimations as the actual value in milliequivalents per litre together with the normal range. My conception of a good piece of paper to get back from the laboratory with respect to acid-base balance would be one which gives the actual plasma bicarbonate, the CO_2 tension, pH and standard bicarbonate or its equivalent. Whether one is given standard bicarbonate as estimated, standard bicarbonate as calculated or blood buffer base does not matter, I think. The important thing is to have some *measure* of the degree of metabolic acidosis or alkalosis. Clinicians nowadays when presented with an estimate of plasma electrolytes in milliequivalents generally say, well all right, we had better give some sodium. Quite often they have a scheme for giving so many litres of saline intravenously. Well, within reason, there is no reason why they should not do the same thing for bicarbonate.

Chairman: Thank you, Mr. Ludbrook. I certainly was fascinated by Dr. Astrup's diagram, which I think can be described as a diagram to end all diagrams. It might perhaps be a little too complicated to let loose on the clinician until he has been well educated, but I rather understand that Dr. Astrup has another slide in his pocket which he would like to show us now.

Astrup: You must determine three values to evaluate acid-base disturbances. P_{CO_2} and pH are of some value concerning the metabolic aspects. The diagram we use in Copenhagen (Fig. 1) is an ordinary log P_{CO_2} and pH diagram. You have 12 different conditions in the acid-base metabolism. In the middle you have the pH normal values, normal values for P_{CO_2} and normal values for the slope of the curve, for standard bicarbonate. If we move over to the left side we have an acidosis. If we are on the right side, alkalosis. Now I can just go through a few of them. If we are in No. 12 we have uncompensated respiratory acidosis. Here the standard bicarbonate is higher than normal, the pH is lower than normal—the last means that there is an acidosis—the P_{CO_2} is higher than normal so this must be a partly compensated respiratory acidosis. In No. 3 we have a fully compensated respiratory acidosis, in No. 7 we have a metabolic alkalosis, in No. 10 we have a partly metabolic acidosis and so on. We are going to print the dif-

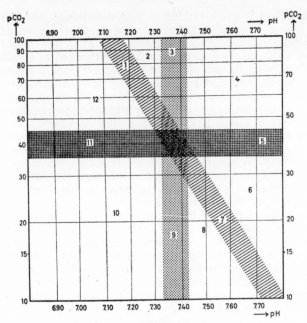

FIG. 1. For explanation, see text.

ferent diagnoses on the back of the paper so that the clinicians can just see the diagnoses. Then we will give a value for Δ acid or Δ base, as I told you earlier, so by the formulas which we also will write down, the clinicians can find out how much acid or base they have to give the patient in order to get a normal value for standard bicarbonate.

Campbell: I was going to ask Dr. Astrup earlier about a point of terminology we have not settled. I think he is in a slightly difficult situation logically with the definitions he gave us earlier this afternoon about acidosis and alkalosis. You defined them in terms of a change in pH. You cannot, therefore, have a fully compensated acidosis, can you?

Astrup: That is complicated.

Campbell: I would just ask the meeting if there is any strong objection to using acidosis and alkalosis for changes which, if there were no compensation, would produce a disturbance of pH and restrict the terms acidæmia and alkalæmia to indicate whether in fact the pH is disturbed from the normal range or not.

Chairman: That seems eminently logical to me. Dr. Severinghaus?

Severinghaus: In answer to that, is it ever found that a respiratory acidosis is completely compensated?

Campbell: Oh, yes. I could tell you of people running along with P_{CO_2}'s of 60 and pH's of 7·35. And in any case, if you define it in terms of a deviation from normal and then remove the deviation from normal you have removed the definition.

Severinghaus: I think those who have objected to this type of plot, which I think is very good, on the basis of the fact that it is a logarithm, really ought to withdraw that objection because that is not a log P_{CO_2} plot. If it were the top would be 2·0 not 100, and then everybody would be confused. This is just P_{CO_2}. It happens to be plotted on a sort of slippery scale. I do not think the scale is going to confuse anyone, it just makes it more easy to read.

Chairman: Well, none of us, not even the simplest clinician, boggles at pH, but pH is, of course, a logarithmic plot anyway.

Hill: There is one small point that should be made if you are going to agree that more pH measurements should be taken. As we have representatives of the manufacturers here, I would point out that if this method is going to come into general use we ought to think in terms of economics. Many of us use pH meters which cost over £200, and in talking to Dr. Astrup he mentioned that possibly his apparatus would come up somewhere round about £300, which is quite a lot of money, and we do hope that out of this meeting some sort of specification will emerge. We hope we will persuade the manufacturers to give us pH meters at a reasonably economic price which will not do more than you really need, otherwise I fail to see how these measurements are going to become more generally used than they are at present.

Chairman: That is a very important point. We did refer to this earlier in the discussion. The question is: should we have two standards of accuracy, one for clinical use and one for laboratory use? I am going to vote for it. I think it is a good idea because it will mean that the man who works in the laboratory and can get money from his supporting organization can get the Rolls Royce or the Cadillac among pH meters, and the clinician who is content with the lower order of accuracy can have a pH meter which will be good enough for his purposes, and which may well be £100–£150 cheaper.

Mattock: Mr. Lauchlan will probably have some things to say as well, but I think we shall be united in one thing, and that is that the manufacturers themselves would be very happy if they know what the clinicians wanted. One of the big problems we have, and I am very serious about this, is that we just do not know what people want. The reasons for this are manifold, I think. One is the fact that we come in contact with two types of people whom I have already described as being the ·001 group and the ·02 group. We ourselves in the manufacturers' laboratories come in contact with the ·001 group rather more than the ·02 group. It is our representatives who come in contact with the ·02 group. In making instruments available we would certainly like an indication of the order of discrimination required, whether or not two groups of instruments are to be encouraged, and the general techniques in so far as electrodes are concerned which are likely to be of interest. I think it is unfair to us to be led up the garden to adopt certain electrode arrangements and certain techniques which in fact may be out of date or which may become out of date in a very short time. Inevitably, when you are manufacturing an article there is a delay between receiving it and getting it on to the market. If this occurs with a system which perhaps is not going to be adopted anyway or which for some reason does not find favour, then we are going to be put further back by then having to turn round and get on to the system that *is* going to be used. And in that sense it would help us very considerably if there were some indication, perhaps a little better than we have had so far, of the way in which these measurements are going so that we can act accordingly. I think Mr. Lauchlan would agree with that.

Lauchlan: I would like to amplify that. It is a matter of economics always. The elaborate pH meter must cost more. If more are wanted and more people are able to use the ·001 then we shall make more of those meters and the price must come down. If we could possibly get some idea of the quantity of the special pH meters that might be wanted, then we could decide how far we could go: perhaps cut the price on the first ones and hope to make up on the total number. If you are only going to make a few they will be expensive. Mr. Chairman, I would like also, if I may as a layman, to butt in on diagrams. I think all of us will agree that in the instructions on instruments for people quite unacquainted with their use, diagrams and pictures of various sorts are of far more value for instructing the user than any amount of typescript written. A picture or diagram of what the thing does will present a far better idea. Many people have not time or patience to read through a lot of manuscript, but the diagram will show at a glance.

Pask: Could I say just another word on this education matter? It has always seemed to me odd that the physiologist or biochemist in the hospital is never given a chance to explain. If you had an electrocardiograph done you would not expect to be told that the T wave was so many millivolts and the QTC was so and so. The report in most hospitals contains also some helpful advice such as: " Subject to clinical examination I think this patient is dead." I very much like Dr. Astrup's remark that he was going to print the diagnoses on the back because this is the way that education spreads. I wonder if it could not go a bit further. There is an attractive term in the United States—soda water is known as carbonated water. I wonder if we might be able to say: " Your patient is too car-bonated because he has not enough fresh air," which would, you know, really get the thing around.

Campbell: The first thing I was going to say was that I do not really think that the argument is between a diagram and giving a number. There is no mutual exclusion. You can give both. It is not like some of the other things we have discussed where you have to do one or the other. You can give both and I think we need not worry ourselves, we can try both and see which finds more favour. The thing I would like to do, very respectfully, Sir, is disagree with you about setting two standards. I think it presupposes that there is in fact a simple relationship between lack of care and loss of accuracy, whereas in many situations the relationship is an extremely complicated one and lack of care will land you a mile away as easily as land you a yard away. I think this goes in pH work probably more than in any other field, and I would not like personally to have people saying they would accept two standards in this sort of thing.

Cliffe: On this question of the accuracy of the instrument it would seem to me that by contrast with the requirements of industry, there is a very special requirement here in that our whole range of pH measurement is obviously within half a pH unit and it would not therefore seem to me very sensible to have a pH meter which we could not rely on to at least ·01 of a pH unit and that is not a simple instrument; and I think that the companies that have taken this up, particularly Cambridge and E.I.L., have done a great service to the profession in giving us instruments like the " Vibron " which are reliable within those limits. I think that as soon as we relax that we get into the ordinary range of commercial pH meters, and after all the industrialist is quite happy with the pH to ·1 of a unit. That seems to me to be the other class of instrument and to differentiate between one which perhaps gives you ·03, ·04 or ·01 down to ·001 on the other hand, would be a bit unrealistic from the manufacturers' point of view and from our point of view in price. Medical people want an instrument which will work reliably, which will always work and will work simply. They just have not had it, until recent years, from the manufacturer. We have exactly the same sort of trouble in the blood pressure field and I think it is only in the last few years that we have got instruments that we really can rely on and that is why there is the difference of opinion, because the instruments have not been up to the standard we require. I would suggest from a practical point of view to the manufacturers here that we would not want an instrument that we could not rely on to at least ·01 of a pH. Another point I may make is a hangover from yesterday's discussion, and this is the question of having another standard buffer. I do agree with Dr. Campbell that we are going to reduce our measurement errors if we can get one which is somewhere in the mid-range of blood pH and it might be in order for a recommendation from this meeting to go to a suitable committee—possibly the British Standards or the National Physical Laboratory or some authority—who could put into being the production of a new standard which is specific for our use.

Wright: If I may go back to pH meters again, I think this might be one circumstance where it would be worth economizing by sacrificing versatility rather than accuracy. The apparatus for measuring blood pH will, most probably, never be used for anything else. One could make a suitable pH meter as accurate as possible and yet save money by cutting down its range and versatility.

Chairman: With regret I must now draw these proceedings to a close. The fears which I put forward have to some extent, I think, been realized. We have not come away able to say to ourselves: " Well, we have settled that problem." I think it would have been very optimistic of anyone to imagine that we would do so. We have had a very profitable discussion and we have had an exchange of ideas. We have a much better idea than we had before what other people are thinking about and how their minds are working. We have had a fascinating glimpse into the future and we hope that future will not be too far away. I think we can say that it has been a successful meeting. As Chairman of it I would like to express my thanks to all of you who have taken part in it and made it so. I would like, too, to express our thanks to Mrs. Hart Dyke who has been busily recording the pearls of wisdom which in due course will be strung to make a shining necklace. We have all been impressed, I know, by the efficiency of the organization of this meeting and by the comfort of our surroundings. Unfortunately sickness has struck down both the Director of the Ciba Foundation, Dr. Wolstenholme, and now his deputy, Dr. Genese, but I would like to express to them in their absence—through Miss Etherington who is here as their representative—and to Miss Chator who has been working the tape and to Mr. Winter who has been showing the slides, our gratitude and our appreciation for arranging this Conference and for putting their incomparable organization at our disposal.

Campbell: Before we go, I think we must all thank you very much for organizing this. We must also thank you very much for being such a good Chairman, and I will ask the Group to break your rule and show our appreciation (APPLAUSE).

XIV. DEMONSTRATION OF EQUIPMENT

At a demonstration held in connection with the Conference the following equipment was exhibited:

Dr. Astrup: Apparatus for determining pH, P_{CO_2} and standard bicarbonate in micro-samples of capillary blood.

Cambridge Instrument Co. Ltd., 13 Grosvenor Place, London, S.W.1.

1. Bench pH meter.
2. Direct reading pH indicator.
3. Dye dilution recorder.
4. Glass electrode for use on heart-lung machine.
5. Stadie blood electrode system.
6. Murray blood electrode system.
7. Stomach electrode system.

Dr. Campbell:

1. The " Ird-O-Meter "—a respiratory CO_2 analyser manufactured by the Infra Red Development Co. Ltd., Welwyn Garden City, Herts. This instrument may be used for the monitoring of the expired CO_2 concentration, the measurement of the end tidal CO_2 concentration and the measurement of mixed venous CO_2 tension by the rebreathing technique.
2. Simplified Haldane Gas Analyser: A modification of the standard Haldane apparatus for the estimation of CO_2 only. A number of detailed alterations have made the apparatus simpler to make, easier to understand and quicker to operate. Duplicate estimations can be performed in three minutes with an accuracy of at least $\pm$ 0·1 per cent. The instrument is to be made by Aimer Products, Rochester Place, Camden Town, London, N.W.1.

Electronic Instruments Ltd., Lower Mortlake Road, Richmond, Surrey.

1. The Wynn-E.I.L. electrode system.
2. The Mendel-E.I.L. electrode system.
3. The E.I.L. heart-lung electrode system.
4. The E.I.L. microflow electrode system.
5. E.I.L. pH meters for blood pH measurement.

Dr. Nunn:

1. A tonometer for equilibrating samples of blood with gas mixtures of known composition at 38° C.
2. A technique for withdrawing the blood sample from the tonometer without changing the temperature, pressure or composition of the gas in contact with the blood.
3. A centrifuge for separating blood at 38° C out of contact with the air.
4. Astrup's method for determination of P_{CO_2} of separated plasma by the interpolation technique.

W. G. Pye & Co. Ltd., " Granta " Works, 80 Newmarket Road, Cambridge.

1. " Dynacap " pH meter.
2. External meter with provision for a backing-off voltage to increase the readability of the pH meter.
3. Stadie, Hartree and McInnes Belcher electrodes.
4. Stomach electrodes.
5. Flow assembly for use with a heart-lung machine.

Dr. Severinghaus: Combined electrodes for the measurement of P_{O_2} and P_{CO_2} of blood (*J. appl. Physiol.*, **13**, 515). The apparatus consists of:

1. Constant temperature water bath.
2. CO_2 sensitive electrode, consisting of a glass electrode in contact with a bicarbonate solution separated from blood by a teflon membrane.
3. A Clark oxygen electrode.
4. A small tonometer for preparing blood of known P_{O_2} to calibrate the oxygen electrode.

Dr. Wright:

1. New type of liquid junction and capillary electrode system for pH measurement on small samples.
2. Silver chloride reference electrodes.
3. Replacement silver chloride electrode for the centre of a conventional bulb glass electrode.
4. A capillary microelectrode for implantation in tissues.
5. A chamber for the spinning of 0·1 ml of blood and immediate separation of the cells.

SUBJECT INDEX

PRINTED IN GREAT BRITAIN BY THE WHITEFRIARS PRESS LTD.
LONDON AND TONBRIDGE